A COLORADO CHRISTMAS
ANTHOLOGY

With Special Thanks To:

The Colorado Historical Society Staff, The Denver Public Library Western History Department Staff, The Delta and Durango County Chambers of Commerce, the Jefferson County Libraries: Lakewood and Golden Branches. And to Chris Christofferson; Mary Cook, Colorado Author's League; Bernard Kelly; Lisa Knudsen, Mountain and Plains Booksellers Assn.; Linda Lester; Margaret Maupin, Tattered Cover Bookstore; Cathy Nachtigal, The Book Place of Applewood; Richard Over, 10th Mountain Division Member.

a Colorado Christmas *anthology*

Edited by
Sara Lohaus and Jan White

Partridge Press
St. Cloud, Minnesota

Cover Art: "Here Comes Santa" by Paul Gregg, 1946. Gregg, a staff artist for *The Denver Post* from 1903 until he died in 1949, painted close to a thousand covers for the Sunday magazine section. Used with permission of the Colorado Historical Society.

Editors: Sara Lohaus and Jan White
Associate Editors: Theresa Rice Engels and Sylvia Tiala
Projects Editor: Stephen E. Engels
Original Art: Ethel Boyle, L. Erwin
Cover Design: Jody Chapel, Cover to Cover Design
Typography: North Star Press of St. Cloud, Inc.

ISBN: 0-9621085-0-6
Copyright © 1990 Partridge Press

Printed in the United States of America by Sentinel Printing, Inc.

Partridge Press
P.O. Box 364
St. Cloud, MN 56302
612-253-1145

My reindeer's sick
My sleigh's broke, too,
But live or die,
I'll get to you with
Christmas Greetings.

Anonymous
Louisville, Colorado
1922

CONTENTS

AS WITH GLADNESS MEN OF OLD
Keeping Christmas in Times Past

LET THERE BE PEACE ON EARTH
The Essence of Christmas

THE CHILDREN WERE NESTLED ALL SNUG IN THEIR BEDS

Christmas Through A Child's Eyes

I'LL BE HOME FOR CHRISTMAS

Cherishing the Memories

CHRISTMAS FOR COWBOYS
At Home on the Range

OH BRING US SOME
FIGGY PUDDING
Celebrating the Feast

DECK THE HALLS

Christmas Celebrations Then & Now

Newspaper accounts of Christmas in Colorado: *The Daily Sentinel, The Denver Post, The Daily Rocky Mountain News, The Georgetown Miner, The Delta County Independent, The Pueblo Star Journal Sunday Chiefton, The Denver Republican, The Denver Times, The Steamboat Pilot.* Also *Colorado Magazine* and *Colorado Homes and Lifestyles*

AS WITH GLADNESS MEN OF OLD

Keeping Christmas in Times Past

Star of Empire Guides the Way

It was Christmas the year of our Lord 1858 when men with new dreams, new visions, were following another Star across another plain to the Birth of a new Empire. They had come out of the East, their goal another village.

If to these men traveling into the Unknown this dream may have seemed an illusion, so may have that dream which led the Wise Men that Night into Bethlehem. They who had led the way across the trail-less Frontier must have had faith beyond understanding and on that Christmas of '58 they must have been thinking of that First Christmas because they talked about the Star of Hope as their guide and one among them of great faith said:

Westward the Star of Empire takes its way and now hangs bright over the Rocky Mountains.

—S. S. Curtis

Edith Eudora Kohl, *Denver's First Christmas*

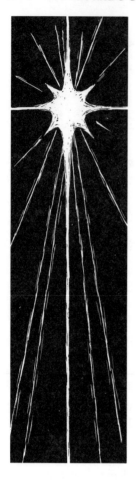

O star of wonder, star of night
Star with royal beauty bright
Westward leading, still proceeding
Guide us to thy perfect light

Pike's Yuletide Feast

We now again found ourselves all assembled together on Christmas Eve, and appeared generally to be content although, all the refreshment we had to celebrate that day with, was buffalo meat without salt, or any other thing whatever.

We spent the day [Christmas] as agreeably as could be expected from men in our situation.

Zebulon Pike, *Journal of a Voyage*

Fifty-two years prior to the settlement at Denver, Zebulon Montgomery Pike, the first of Colorado's military explorers, was hungry, tattered and lost in the Rockies at the approach of Christmas in 1806. His band of explorers rejoined the base party at the site of Pueblo and proceeded up the Arkansas River, expecting to find its source.

But Pike and his companions had seen enough. They had not eaten for two days and their thin cotton overalls were ragged. Lacking socks, the men had cut their blankets into strips to wind about their legs. They hurried downstream and found the rest in a merry mood on a cloudy Christmas Eve. Just when they had seemed about to starve for lack of game, eight fat buffalo had waddled by.

So Christmas Day, 1806, was for feasting around a log fire big enough to warm much of their campsite four miles above present Salida and under Cameron Mountain. The Captain donned his dress uniform—faded blue trousers, scarlet cap and red coat lined with fox skins, but the elegant effect was reduced by his bare toes sticking out from what was left of his moccasins. The starving celebrants gorged on the buffalo meat and sent Christmas carols ringing across valley.

> This interpretation of Colorado's first recorded Christmas celebration is from: *The Pueblo Star-Journal Sunday Chieftain, Dec. 20, 1970, and The Great Gates*, by Marshall Sprague, Colorado Springs, author of many historical novels.

They Held Their Tin Cups High
by Mike Flanagan

On December 21, 1858, a group of miners at the Cherry Creek diggings came across a calendar and got the shock of their lives: there were only four shopping days until Christmas. Unseasonably warm temperatures and an insatiable lust for riches had almost overshadowed the holiday completely. With typical frontier spirit, they planned a celebration out on the edge of nowhere, just west of present Aurora, Colorado. Little did they know, but even Santa Claus was coming to town.

And it came to pass in those days that wise men and foolish alike rushed Out West searching not for frankincense and myrrh, but for gold. They followed no star, just a slogan that said "Pikes Peak or Bust." Most would do the latter.

They set up their tents and shacks on either side of Cherry Creek and began panning for the shiny dust. Two townsites were incorporated in the autumn of 1858. Auraria on the west was mostly transplanted Georgians. On the east, Denver City was made up of Kansans who had come with Gen. William Larimer. When Capt. R. A. Spooner's party from Nebraska and Iowa arrived on November 4, the region was already being called the "New Eldorado." By Christmas though, no one had struck it rich. Now the talk concerned waiting for the spring thaw and getting to the mountains. There, they would surely find the yellow ore.

In the meantime, someone in the Spooner camp had discovered the calendar and, just for kicks, decided to see what day it was. Immediate holiday depression set in. Here they were, 600 miles from a railroad and 200 miles from the nearest post office at Ft. Laramie, Wyoming. (Enterprising trader Jim Sanders became the Denver postal service on November 23, agreeing to carry letters to Wyoming for $.50 per piece. He would bring the return mail, Christmas cards and all, on January 8.)

There were some 200 men, five women (four of them married), and perhaps a half-dozen children in this 60-day old metropolis. All were sure they were not included on Santa's map. Why, who had ever heard of such a map, with names like Larimer, Curtis, Stout, and Wynkoop?

As the Denver doldrums cast a pallor over the yule season, a jolly old elf slowly made his way toward the encampment. Richens Wootton and his wife were driving two ox carts from what seemed as far away as the North Pole—Fort Union, New Mexico. A merchant by trade, he hoped to be a peddler just opening his pack in the new city. In the back of one wagon, he knew he was carrying *the* hot item for the Christmas of 1858, resting comfortably next to his two sleeping children. If the weather held and the creek didn't rise, he just might make town by, say, December 25.

Back in Denver, the mood had improved. French Count Henri Murat was making arrangements to host an open log cabin. His German bride Katerina baked cookies and molded candles for a tree that was being imported from the foothills.

In the Spooner camp, as glowingly reported by correspondent A. O. McGrew to the *Omaha Times*, a pioneer Christmas dinner with all the trimmings filled the air with heavenly scents. Three cooks named Sullivan, Crum, and Frary were putting together an impressive menu of buffalo, ham, venison, elk tongue, bear meat, rabbit, wild turkey, squirrel, quail, baked potatoes, beans, rice, and biscuits. Their gourmet dessert tray would include dried mountain plums, apple and peach pie and rice pudding. (In such spare times one must wonder if this array was cooked up in the Spooner kitchen or in the brain of McGrew, but suffice to say, a celebration was in the offing.)

Christmas morning was recorded as "soft and genial as a May day, as beautiful as ever shone. Not a breeze whispered through the leafless cottonwoods." It was calm, and one could easily hear the sound of wagon wheels and the prancing and pawing of each oxen hoof. According to Henry Edward Warner in a 1900 *Denver Times*, "The sun had just rubbed its sleepy eyes and peeped in on the little settlement . . . when Santa Claus made his appearance."

Wootton unloaded his goods and set up his tent. That task completed, he rolled out a barrel from one of the wagons and cracked the top with an axe. Inside was Taos Lightning, a potent moonshine guaranteed to start an electrical storm in the head. It was the first whiskey in the diggings. Said Warner, "it went down like a swain on his knees to the object of his affections. It hit the stomach all in a lump and sent cheerful feeling up to the roots of a fellow's hair and back again to his toes, in one howling, rip-roaring succession of luxurious vibratory spasms of exquisite joy. It beat grand opera without even trying."

"Uncle Dick gave the whole town a free blowout," said witness A. E. Pearce. "Everyone helped himself freely, using tin cups." Larimer's son, 18-year-old William, said, "Several did help themselves, and so often that they needed help to reach their cabins." According to the General, Methodist Rev. George W. Fisher's plans for a religious service were dashed: "Some were in favor, some were lukewarm and some opposed entirely to the program. This opposition grew when that arch opponent of religion, whiskey, was introduced."

There would be no football games; a wrestling match for two yoke of oxen and a wagon was quickly arranged.

A bonfire and hoedown began in the streets. Men locked arms and danced to songs like "The Star-Spangled Banner," "The Girl I Left Behind Me," and a new tune, composed by McGrew, called "Root, Hog, or Die." "Active feet went into motion," he wrote, "and in the weird light we danced until midnight. Groups of Indians with their squaws and papooses filled the shadowy background. It was a picture that Rembrandt would have loved." Meanwhile, at the Murat cabin, guests including Mrs. Wootton and her children decorated the Christmas tree and sang "Silent Night."

As for the most popular man in town, he was called "Uncle Dick" from that day on, given a full share in the Auraria Town Company, and land on which he would build his business. He made sure none of the celebrators drove home that night—many settled down for a long winter's nap on the banks of Cherry Creek.

What we know about that first Denver Christmas of 1858 has been obscured by visions of sugarplums over the years. We can bet our stockings that Colorado's first bash was a beaut. In dignity and stupor, the pioneers held their tin cups high to a future bright with promise in a transitory time that vanished quickly, like the ghost of Christmas past.

Mike Flanagan, a Denver Freelance Writer, has published two books, Out West *and* Days Of The West. *He also wrote a column titled "Out West" for The Denver* Post *for seven years.*

Platte River Gold Diggings Bill Of Fare
Christmas 1858

Soups:
Oyster soup. Ox tail.

Fish:
Salmon trout, with oyster sauce

Boiled
Corned beef, buffalo tongue, mutton, pork, ham, beef tongue, elk tongue.

Roast.
Venison, a la mode; buffalo smothered; antelope; beef; mutton; pork; grizzly bear, a la mode; elk; mountain sheep; mountain pig.

Game.
Mountain pheasants; mountain rabbits; turkeys; ducks; sage hen; prairie chickens; black mountain squirrel, prairie dog; snipe; mountain rats; white swans; quails; sand hill cranes.

Extras.
Potatoes baked; potatoes boiled; rice; beans, baked and boiled; beets; squashes, fried; pumpkins, stewed.

Dessert:
Mince pie, currant pie, apple pie; rice pie; peach pie; mountain cranberry pie; tapioca pudding; bread pudding; rice pudding.

Fruits.
Brazil nuts; almonds, hazel nuts; filberts; pecans; wild currants; raisins; prickly pear; dried mountain plum.

Wine List.
Hockheimer; madeira; champagne; golden sherry; cherry bounce; hock; Monongahela whiskey; claret; brandy; Scotch whiskey; Ja. rum; Bourbon whiskey; Taos lightning.*

Pioneer Celebrations Are Born

by John Monnett

Despite the romance and glory that history has ascribed to the hardships experienced by the first U.S. explorers in the Rocky Mountain West, in reality, they were like any soldiers who have spent months or years away from home, stationed on some far-flung frontier of the world. At Christmastime melancholy deeply pervaded their thoughts and emotions. As they were not intent upon settling permanently in the new land, they left very little of cultural significance. They established no ritual Christmas traditions in the wilderness they explored. Yet over the trails they blazed and through the great mountain passes they discovered were to come thousands of pioneers, who would conquer the West. The founders of towns and cities throughout the Rocky Mountain empire could not have succeeded if it were not for the efforts of these early government explorers—they opened the gates of civilization. And through the magnificent portals that are the Rocky Mountains there would pass a host of trappers, traders, miners, and town builders. Herdsman and farmer would settle the grassy flanks of the regal peaks, and they would bring with them rich cultural traditions from every corner of the young nation and from exotic foreign lands. Soon the lusty pioneers would break down the forbidden barriers of the old Spanish empire in the Southwest, absorbing the profuse and luxuriant traditions of Spain and Mexico in the process. Epochal customs of Christmas took root, mixing and adapting in a multicultural backdrop, and rising from bold forests, mountain peaks, and prairie wilderness that gave character to the country and the men and women who settled there. Within the span of a century the Rocky Mountains would boast some of the most colorful celebrations of Yuletide to be found anywhere in the world.

John Monnett, is a Western history professor at Metropolitan State College and University of Colorado, Denver.

Christmas Wolves on the
Arkansas River: 1863

The spirit of Christmas, always found in lowly places, was present in the home of one pioneer Colorado family in the winter of *1863*. The story of its coming is told by Mrs. Loretta H. Rich who was a little girl then and whose efforts were largely responsible for it's presence.

Mrs. Rich had come, with her parents, two younger brothers and three younger sisters, to Colorado in 1859. The winter of 1863 found them in a mining camp on the Arkansas river between where the towns of Buena Vista and Salida now stand.

Loretta, as the oldest child, helped her father in his mining operations. They were taking gold from river sand bars with a rocker. The work was heavy, but the little girl liked it as it kept her in the open.

She also enjoyed the companionship with her father, for the two were great pals. Their diggings were about a mile from the log shack in which they lived.

Early in the fall the family had been cut off from all communication with the outside world by heavy snows. Although they had plenty to eat, there was little variety. Prospects for Christmas were depressing, and they were all quite discouraged. Memories of the previous happy holiday in Central City did not help matters, either.

However, with the dawning of Christmas morning, Loretta did get an inspiration. With the help of brothers and sisters, she brought out linen and china which had come across the plains from their Nebraska home, and served a dinner in the open. Mock turkey and dressing, concocted from beef, black bread and gravy made with shorts, all without salt; beans, and substitute coffee, made from browned bran, were served. Two miner neighbors were invited to the feast, and the parents were the guests of honor.

A wild snow battle followed the meal, and the remainder of the beans were eaten for supper before the youngsters went back to the shack for the night. There Loretta told her father what a fine day she had had and how easy it would be to go to work again on the morrow.

However the father said there would be no work next day. The fire, usually laid each night to thaw out the ground for the next day's operations, had not been lighted. Loretta did not know the meaning of fear so she inveigled her sister into going with her to the working grounds. Fuel had been laid the evening before so it would be a small matter to set it afire.

The little girls carried several torches of pitch pine that had been made earlier in the day. One of these was thrown into the waiting pile of brush and as it blazed up they were startled by a weird howl. There, in the circle of light, sat a huge gray wolf and his howl was answered from a distance by his mate.

Loretta thought quickly. She knew that wild animals were afraid of fire but she also knew that the one she had just lighted would not blaze very long. It would burn down to coals that would smolder all night. Before that happened, she must have her sister home.

Cautioning the younger girl not to be afraid and to be careful not to fall, she lighted the extra torches, gave her sister one, and holding her hand, started to run home. As they neared the shanty one of the miners took a shot at the wolf who was following but afraid to approach too, near the blazing torches. The animal was wounded but got away.

In telling of her adventure—the parents were so relieved that there was no thought of punishment for the escapade—Loretta insisted that she had not been frightened, that it was only exertion that made her face so white.

Later she confessed to her father that she really had been terribly scared, but she couldn't let her younger brothers and sisters know.

Mrs. Rich, who is now nearly 80 years old, says she truly found the spirit of Christmas that day—it lies in trying to make others happy—and, while she is soon to celebrate the sixty-sixth Christmas since that one, she has never had one she enjoyed more.

Good Hopes for the Future . . .
A Christmas Letter

Denver, December 25, 1870

Feeling in a rather talkative and meditative mood, I have ventured to say a word to you about old times. 'Tis well once in a while to retrospect, look back over the past, and gather lessons, for guidance in the future. This thirteenth Christmas for you and me in the Rocky Mountain country, brings to mind many of the events of the early days in this "wilderness" of America. I am remembering, when you arrived with the NEWS press and type; of the rival to claim the credit of first starting a paper in the new gold fields of the great mountains; how you commenced and published and fought and published again through all the dark days that preceded and followed, the "REIGN OF TERROR," in Denver; of your triumph, and the discomfiture of your enemies. Then of the attempted rending asunder of the government, and the unity of our country; the troublous (sic) times that have followed; then the defeat and utter demoralization and route of the foes of the republic; and on through Indian wars, and other difficulties until finally the "Iron Horse" has roused us from our lethargy. And now, on this bright Christmas, after all the toil, danger, trouble and delay, we begin to realize the fulfillment of our hopes.

The days for which we have hoped are rapidly coming; they are even here, and soon the "Pike's Peak country" of the "early days" will be the State of Colorado, rich and prosperous. "The gem of the continent," "The Queen" of the "Golden stores of the Union," justly entitled to this appellation on account of her long lines of railroads, her thousands of acres of well cultivated fields, her "cattle on a thousand hills," her mines of gold and silver in every mountain and mills in every gulch, and last her beautiful cities in mountains and on plains.

Well, the Christmas is past noon, and dinner is near ready, so here's congratulation on the past and good hopes for the future in a cup of nice "hot stuff."

Yours Truly,

John B.

Safe At Home For Christmas

Christmases in Routt County go back to 1886, in the memories of Miss Laura Monson of Steamboat Springs. On September first of that year her father, his wife and six children, of whom she was the eldest, came to Pleasant Valley where they took up a homestead.

The first Christmas was an anxious time which Miss Monson will never forget. Her father, with Mr. Nichols and Dick Fussel, a young man, who with his wife, had followed the Monsons to Pleasant Valley, had gone to Steamboat Springs on the morning of the 23rd, for what Christmas treats he might be able to find and carry home on skis.

When a heavy storm set in next day and the three men failed to return by nightfall, their families feared for their lives. Christmas morning was a bleak one in the two cabins, as the three wives and the Monson children watched the snow falling and blowing, and wondered whether the three men would ever return. Even the younger children realized the seriousness of the situation and felt the tense anxiety.

Shortly before noon on Christmas Day the men reached home. Night and the blizzard had overtaken them as they reached Grouse Creek and they dared not go on. Digging down through three feet of snow to the bare ground, they burned willows through the night, and with the snow wall around them to keep in the heat, they escaped without freezing either hands or feet.

Father's safe arrival home made Christmas enough, that year, regardless of the pack he carried, containing all the sweets he could find in the town, which wasn't much, at that.

But Mother Monson was inventive and made the most of what they had. She saved deer tallow to make pies and biscuits, later learning that bear grease mixed with deer tallow made better shortening. She made doughnuts, the first they had all winter, rolling them in precious sugar—a treat to be remembered.

Steamboat Pilot, January 4, 1940

Reflecting on Christmas 1859, and her first winter in Denver, Mrs. William N. Byers told a newspaper reporter, "You know we didn't get homesick, we simply wouldn't let ourselves be that. Pioneers are not the homesick kind."

Rocky Mountain News, December 25, 1963

An English Woman Goes West, December 1871

Denver looks wintry enough, under six inches to a foot of snow; but it is full of life and bustle. The toy-shops are gay with preparations for Christmas trees; the candy stores are filled with the most attractive sweetmeats; the furriers display beaver coats, and mink, ermine and sable, to tempt the cold passer-by; and in the butcher's shops hang, beside the ordinary beef and mutton, buffalo, black-tailed deer, antelope, Rocky Mountain sheep, quails, partridges, and prairie-chicken.

The streets are full of sleighs, each horse with its collar of bells; and all the little boys have manufactured or bought little sleds, which they tie to the back of any passing cart or carriage; and get whisked along the street until some sharp turn or unusual roughness in the road upsets them.

We found plenty of old friends up here, and have made many more since we came. In the frank unconventional state of society which exists in the West, friendships are made much more easily than even in the eastern states, or still more, in our English society; and, if one wants to have, as the Americans express it, a "good time," one must expand a little out of one's insularity, and meet the hearty good-will shown one with some adequate response.

On Friday evening we went out for a sleigh-drive, the first I have ever had; and most delightful it was. We were muffled up in blankets and buffalo robes and all of our furs. The thermometer was two degrees below zero; the moon as clear as day; and, with a capital pair of horses, we flew over the smooth sparkling snow, our sleigh-bells jingling in the frosty air.

From A Diary *by Rose Kingsley, an Englishwoman living in Colorado Springs, 1871-72.*

Snow Flakes Falling

Falling, falling, softly falling,
Tiny snow-flakes pure and white,
Tell us, have ye any message,
That ye bring this Holy night?
Coming, coming, He is coming,
Surely, surely it is meet
That we spread this spotless carpet,
For the little stranger's feet.

Loving snow-flakes, who is coming?
Who so pure, and good and true?
Surely, surely, loving children
Should prepare to greet Him too.
Here is strife and here is sorrow,
Here are toils that never cease,
Yet He comes, the Christ-Child cometh,
And He brings the Christmas peace.

He is coming? Then we'll seek Him,
Kneel before one little King,
Ask of Him the gift so precious,
That those baby fingers bring,
Yet whose lives are bright and joyous
Joy when shared, alone is sweet;
Go where lonely hearts need loving,
There ye will the Christ-Child meet.

Carol Hymnal, *St. Mark's Episcopal Church, Denver, 1890's*

Millie's Orphans
by Effie Amicarella

Oh the wonder of a year . . .

The Spring of 1921 had come and gone in Denver, little remembered for its season of rebirth and bloom, for that spring my mother died of pneumonia and we three children became orphans. Grandmother Melching had taken us by the hand and led us around the corner to her home, gently pronouncing that we would now live with her and grandfather. Our mother, Millie Melching Martin, was their oldest daughter and we would now forever be "Millie's Orphans." Imagine how Grandmother, Augusta Pauline Melching, felt as a 50 year old woman about to embark on raising these three young siblings: Gertrude Louise, 8 years old; Effie Mae, 6 years old; and Harold William, 2 years old. She still had Elsa, her youngest, at home who would soon be "sister" instead of "Auntie."

Christmas 1921 arrived, our first at Grandmother's house. It would be a far cry from the usual orange, ribbon candy and apple Christmas. On December 6th, the German observance of Christmas began in our house with preparations each day leading up to the culmination on December 25th. Each day new stories were told, old traditions honored, as in the old country.

I can smell the spice of the wonderful gingerbread Santas that Grandmother would bake. Back then you could buy paper Victorian Santas that "glued" on the cookie with frosting. We used them as edible decorations. During this time before Christmas we each made, in great secrecy, something for each member of the family . . . a special gift.

The Christmas tree was trimmed and placed in the living room front window to be shared with others. I remember the frosted glass Santa that clipped on the tree but never hung too straight because it was top-heavy. Then there were the yellow clip-on canaries and the red glass pine cones sprinkled with white glittery snow . . . just a few of the prized ornaments collected through the years and hung with care. Our "new" ornament, added each year, was held in delight. Oh, the wait for Christmas morning!

We always wore long black stockings held up by garters and attached to long underwear. On Christmas Eve these stockings were hung, but never with "great expectations." On Christmas morning Grandfather and Grandmother added the candles to the tree while their newly-formed family watched. Each candle was clipped in place and lit. A silence embraced us in those ten minutes or so that the candles were allowed to burn . . . a remembering time, but also a time to be thankful for "now."

Oh the wonder of it all!

As the candles were snuffed, our excitement grew about the exchange of our special gifts made for one another. Truly it was exciting to give! As we awed over each person's efforts, music filled the room. Grandfather loved opera and most of our records were by famous German opera stars. That Christmas day it was "Adeste Fideles" and "O Tannenbaum" played time after time.

But for Millie's orphans Christmas had only begun!

Grandfather, William C. Melching, a fine sailor who outfitted the Denver Police and Fire Departments, was "going through the chairs" of the B.P.O.E. (Elks), and our Mother had been a devoted Pythian Sister. That Christmas day both organizations arrived bringing wondrous gifts to us.

Harold, although only two years old, became the proud owner of a complete train set. He played with it for years to come, and years later he continues to enjoy it with his own sons.

For sister and me? Effie and Louise received matching red-haired china dolls, rather like the two little sisters they'd been choosen for. We delighted in the doll buggy we would share as we mothered those dolls that had no equals. We still have them today, after nearly 70 years.

Each evening until "little ephiphany," January 12th, the candles on the Christmas tree were lit for a few minutes. And in those precious moments we wondered at the beauty of that there. Much later we would all wonder at the generosity of Grandparents who love and people who care. For the gifts that had been given that Christmas would be remembered and cherished all our lives.

Effie Mae Martin Melching Amicarella was born in 1915 in Denver, CO. After attending West High School and Colorado Women's College, she became a lab technician at St. Luke's Hospital, and later was Head Librarian at Lafayette Public Library for 23 years. She helped found the Lafayette Historical Society and later the Lafayette Miner's Museum.

When a banner is raised on the mountaintop all the people of the earth shall see it. Isaiah 18:3

LET THERE BE
PEACE ON EARTH
The Essence of Christmas

Does Tradition Bind at Christmas?
by Dottie Lamm

I feel Christmas closing in around me. Concentration on any other undertaking is interrupted by holly-gilded thoughts that float in, get pushed away, only to float back again.

What can I get my nephew? Will the packages to the grandparents reach them on time? Is there anything we can get the children that doesn't send video game "zap-zaps" or hard rock electronic chords ricocheting through four floors? Thank heaven "Pink Floyd—The Wall" now will be replaced by traditional Christmas carols on the stereo.

In many ways our children are more traditional than we are. At ages 12 and 15, they want carols at Christmastime, even in place of Pink Floyd. The big tree that we decorate must be done just so; new ornaments are looked at askance. The tiny brass sleds with their engraved names, given to the children when babies, must shine visibly from the front branches. The miniature tree made of pine cones and the ceramic doves have to be placed precisely on the same shelf as last year; each person's stocking hung in the exact designated spot on the fireplace screen. . . .

As the evergreen scent from the formally decorated first floor fills the upstairs of the house, warm memories of last Christmas descend on me, recreating the joyousness of a huge family reunion. Last December at this time I wrote a column anticipating the arrival of relatives: "And this year they are all coming. And I can't wait. . . ."

And they did come, to a traditional old-fashioned Christmas in a big old-fashioned house. We sang carols on Christmas Eve, accompanied by Heather on the piano. We drew names to decide who would fill whose stocking. We recorded on our tape recorder the grandparents' memories of Christmases of old. We dressed up for Christmas dinner, feeling warm and fortunate for the gift of life and the love of each other.

But this year will be different. Last summer, inspired by a recent school-sponsored train trip with Heather, my husband suggested a collective family Christmas present to each other—an Amtrak trip to California. The children agreed enthusiastically, and soon we will depart from Union Station for San Francisco to spend the holiday in the Pacific Heights home of friends who will be skiing in Colorado. Gift certificates will be left for friends and relatives, and we will do the last-minute "stocking" shopping when we reach our destination.

"It just doesn't feel like Christmas," says Heather wistfully as she glances at the ornaments in the storage room still packed in tissue.

"No, it doesn't, but it will when we get there," I answer.

She is still young, too young to know that tradition, though it uplifts our spirits and significantly structures our lives, does not have to bind. Neither does tradition need to be forsaken for new adventure. As the pioneer families of a century ago hauled their lace tablecloths and fine china to the West, we will carry our traditions with us.

We will decorate a tree that our host family is leaving us. Taking with us the little brass sleds. We'll hang our stockings on the mantle and buy our stocking stuffers in Chinatown. We'll sing carols, whether or not there is a piano.

Both children, who were thrilled by the idea of a trip in the sun of last summer, stare longingly at the mountains capped with snow. "How much skiing am I going to miss?" demands Scott. But I am excited. Among the gently interrupting Christmas thoughts invading my consciousness is the long, drawn-out whistle of a train.

I sympathize with our children's recalcitrance. As a child, I loved my Christmases at home; the Christmases which rooted me in the traditions I now pass on. I empathize with their reluctance to travel. Yet I know that the excitement of the trip will slowly, gradually turn the mental tide, that when they hear that train whistle their hearts will race like mine.

This year they will rejoice in our Christmas away. And next Christmas they will rejoice that we again are at home. And so will I.

Colorado's former first lady, Dottie Lamm is a columnist for the Denver Post *and a commentator on the problems facing contemporary women and their families.*

Lullabye for Christmas Eve
by Lois Beebe Hayna

Child, you see only a plane on hold above
Stapleton. Not The Star. Sleep softly.
Footsore camels lose themselves
gratefully, released in favor
of four-wheel drive. The last manger was snapped
up by collectors years ago and who
remembers the address of awestruck shepherds?

I close your window
against jingling and kettled Santas.
The angels' choir may still perform
but will not drown the clink
of money changing hands.

Yet sleep, Child,
sleep. For Christmas never fades.
Good will is, for this season, not
abstract. Feel how it warms your dreams,
arriving on its own,
mysteriously. Hear how it carols
such praise of man and God it makes
adorers of us all, Child. Sleep.

Lois Beebe Hayna is a member of the Poetry Society of America and the Academy of American Poets. She also received a Literary Fellowship from the Colorado Council on the Arts and Humanities. Never Trust A Crow, a collection of poetry, was published in 1990. "Lullabye For Christmas Eve" is presented here for the first time.

A Lady's Life in the Rocky Mountains
by Isabella L. Bird

Every tree was silvered, and the fir-tree tufts of needles looked like white chrysantheumums. The snow lay a foot deep in the gulches, with its hard, smooth surface marked by the feet of innumerable birds and beasts. Ice bridges had formed across all the streams, and I crossed them without knowing when. Gulches looked like fathomless abysses, with clouds boiling up out of them, and shaggy mountain summits, half seen for a moment through the eddies, as quickly vanished. Everything looked vast and indefinite. Then a huge creation, like one of Dore's phantom illustrations, with much breathing of wings, came sailing towards me in a temporary opening in the mist. As with a strange rustle it passed close over my head, I saw, for the first time, the great mountain eagle, carrying a good-sized beast in his talons. It was a noble vision. . . . Birdie, my horse, was covered with exquisite crystals, and her long mane and the long beard which covers her throat were pure white.

. . . I think I never saw such a brilliant atmosphere. That curious phenomena called frost-fall was occurring, in which, whatever moisture may exist in the air, somehow aggregates into feathers and fern leaves, the loveliest of creations, only seen in rarefied air and intense cold. One breath and they vanish. The air was filled with diamond sparks quite intangible. They seemed just glitter and no more. It was still and cloudless, and the shapes of violet mountains were softened by a veil of the tenderest blue.

Estes Park, December, 1873

Choose wisely then, each ornament
And frosted tinsel skein
For branches that have worn jewels
Of gleaming mountain rain.

Elizabeth-Ellan Long

Continental Divide—December
by Enos Mills

After a heavy snowfall, one December morning, I started on skis for two weeks' camping in the Colorado Rockies. The fluffy snow lay smooth and unbroken over the broken mountains. Here and there black pine and spruce trees uplifted arrowheads and snow-cones of the white mantle. On the steep slope, half a mile from my cabin, I was knocked to one side by a barrel mass of snow dropping upon me from a tree, and one ski escaped. As if glad to be off on an adventure of its own, it sped down the mountainside like a shot. It bumped into a low stump, skied high into the air and over a tree-top, and then fell undamaged in the deep snow.

Recovering my runaway ski, I started for the summit of the range, a distance of about nine miles from my cabin. For an hour I followed a stream whose swift waters now and then splashed up through the broken, icy skylights. Then leaving the cañon and skirting the slope, I was on the plateau summit of the Continental Divide, twelve thousand feet above the sea.

One of the country's foremost conservationists and western writers in the late 19th and early 20th centuries, Enos Mills founded Rocky Mountain National Park in 1915.

Colorado Christmas
by The Nitty Gritty Dirt Band

Lookin' out the window of this Hollywood hotel,
You'd never know that it was Christmas Eve.
The billboards and the neon took the place of silver bells
And the temperature is eighty-four degrees.

I can hear the traffic on the crowded strip below,
As the palm trees poke their heads above the scene.
But there's not a single reindeer and it hardly ever snows
And Santa drives a Rolls Royce limousine.

Now all along the Rockies you can feel it in the air,
From Telluride to Boulder down below.
The closest thing to heaven on this planet anywhere,
Is a quiet Christmas mornin' in the Colorado snow.

I remember Christmases when I was just a boy,
In the mornin' I would run to see the tree.
And the carolers on the hillside sang their songs of Christmas Joy,
Well I always thought they sang them just for me.

Now the sun is setting in the California sky
And I can't find the spirit anywhere.
So I think it's time for me to tell Los Angeles good-bye,
I'm goin' back home to look for Christmas there.

'Cause all along the Rockies you can feel it in the air,
From Telluride to Boulder down below.
The closest thing to heaven on this planet anywhere,
It's a quiet Christmas mornin' in the Colorado snow.

The Christmas Box

by Frank Waters

Discouraged and balked at every turn, Rogier finally returned a week before Christmas. The holiday season always had been a big time for the family, and this year, despite an obvious turn in its fortune, everyone seemed to be heading into the stretch for a better one. The blue spruce tree in the front room just tipped the ceiling. Underneath it Sally Lee and Mary Ann kept piling more and more beautifully wrapped presents. Lida was busy all day in the kitchen. The fruit cake had to be prepared two weeks before New Year's Day and set aside to soak up the brandy. Then there were mince pies and chocolate cakes to bake, loaves of bread with crusts browned with butter. Two fifty-pound cans of honey arrived: one of strained honey, and one of hard sugared honey to spread on buckwheat cakes. Then there was cranberry sauce to make, jellies and jams and sauces to be brought up from the basement. And finally, as the tension mounted, the goose and the turkey to be bought and plucked.

"Daddy!" Mrs. Rogier pushed open the door. "Jonathan said he'd left you out here alone. Why, for goodness sakes, it's Christmas Eve! The candles on the tree are lit. Jonathan invited the Grimes down, and Mr. Denman's on the way. Professor Dearson's already here to play the carols the girls are going to sing. Land sakes alive! What can you be thinking of to be so late getting ready?"

It was never out of Rogier's mind, even during the confusion of Christmas morning with everyone tearing open packages, whooping and hollering, drinking egg nogs with every visiting neighbor, watching the baby. The big two o'clock dinner was no relief. He could hardly eat for thinking of Abe and Jake up in their cabin. Why, indeed, hadn't he brought them down if it was going to spoil his whole Christmas, asked Mrs. Rogier. Rogier abruptly gulped down his glass of after-dinner port, flung aside his lace-trimmed napkin, and called Mrs. Rogier into the kitchen.

That little frail woman no doubt had her faults, but she possessed that supreme virtue which permitted the girls to concede her to be what they called a "good sport." Within minutes she had commandeered the help and approbation of the whole family. While

Mary Ann ran for a big striped box, she laid out plenty of turkey, cranberry sauce, rolls, mince pie, candy, nuts—"but Jake hasn't got teeth for" interrupted Rogier. Ona pulled him away. "Daddy, this is going to be a real Christmas box. We're not going to leave out a thing. And we're going to tie it with red and green ribbon!" Mary Ann came whooping in from the front room. She had heard of those two big raw-bones and had stolen off the tree two trinkets to put in the box for them—a monkey on a stick and a small jack-in-the-box.

Rogier, elated, ran with many kisses to catch the late afternoon train. By nightfall he was trudging the steep trail up to Altman, the big box under his arm. The cabin was dark and cold. He lit a fire, adjusted the lamp, and sat down in his overcoat to wait for Abe and Jake.

They came in two hours later, both half-drunk and hilarious, too full to eat a bite. One of General Booth's "Blood and Fire Warriors" had squeezed them into a Salvation Army Christmas Dinner for destitute strikers.

Rogier felt so angry and ashamed that he pitched the box out the back door and went to bed in a huff. Rogier sentimentality! What a fool he had been to miss Christmas night at home with his family!

He was awakened by a stealthy whispering. He rolled over. Abe and Jake were bent over their bunk with lighted matches; they had crawled down the snowy draw and brought back the box. The bottle of port had not been broken, and they were trying to finish it without waking him.

"Hold on!" he cried, jumping out of bed and lighting the lamp. He had suddenly thought of the toys inside. "You two boys have had your Christmas dinner and so have I. But what about the McGees down below? What about them, hey?"

Abe with a shout had discovered the monkey on a stick inside and was trying to trade the jack-in-the-box to Jake for another swig of port. Good-natured and hilarious, they passed the bottle to Rogier and helped him into his boots. Then shortly before midnight, the three men left the cabin and set out. Abe, in front, held up a lantern and the little furred monkey on his stick. Jake, behind, carried the jack-in-the-box and a pick handle. In the middle, surreptitiously sipping port to keep warm, Rogier plunged through the drifts with the huge box.

The trail, greenish white in moonlight, dipped into the shadow of the cliffs. The stars hung low, cold, and brilliant as bottle glass. The trail curved again. A thin wisp of smoke was rising out of McGee's chimney; the fire was not yet out.

Dom! It felt like Christmas night after all!

Regarded as one of the foremost chroniclers of the American West and South-west, Frank Waters has written numerous fiction and nonfiction works dealing with frontier hardships and Indian life. Garnering many honors, he received the Western Heritage Award in 1972 for Pike's Peak: A Family Saga, *the source of this selection.*

Peace on Earth

by Gene Amole

The city is quiet now. Shopping center malls are empty. Traffic signals downtown are like lonely sentinels standing guard over empty streets. There is darkness behind store windows.

Out in the neighborhoods, people scurry through the cold to trash cans with great, crumpled wads of holiday wrapping paper. New bicycles are wobbling along sidewalks. A troubled man climbs wearily into his car and wonders where he'll find D cell batteries on Christmas morning.

The smells of incense, new clothing and cologne mingle in the church. "Hodie Christus Natus Est" echoes down on a fidgety little boy. An infant cries and is hurried from the pew and down the aisle.

The hospital room is quiet, but for the measured wheeze of the little old man asleep on a high, white bed. There is a tube in his nose. On a corner table is a small, plastic Christmas tree. Outside the door, the nurse's shoes squeak rapidly along the empty hall. She frets that there was no time to bake fruitcake or Christmas cookies this year. There is a distant laugh from an opening elevator door.

The kitchen windows of the old north Denver house are fogged with steam. The lights inside are bright and the woman bends over and cracks the oven door. There's a rush of sweet sage aroma. Now, she opens the oven all the way and bastes the breast, legs and wings of the turkey with a plastic syringe.

There's an old Chevy scraping along Kalamath at West 12th

Avenue. The six youths inside are restless and don't know where to go. The runner along the Highline Canal pulls his knit cap down around his ears.

It is Christmas and we don't have to get ready for it anymore. Not for another year. There were private moments this past week that were filled with sadness. On the crowded streets were the lonely for whom fulfillment always seems to fall short of promise. The price of humanness is never greater than at Christmastime.

For the little girl, though, it was difficult to contain her joy. She ran and skipped and impulsively kissed her mother on the cheek. And then her tiny, sticky hand found its way into her father's hand.

The plain, young woman in her east Denver apartment leafed aimlessly through a magazine. She kept looking at the telephone. It wouldn't ring. It just plain wouldn't ring.

A sweet-faced minister on television asked, "Where is he that is born King of the Jews? For we have seen his star in the East, and are come to worship him."

He was in a manger. There had been no room at the inn. There are plenty of rooms at the Holiday Inn this morning and there aren't very many people in the coffee shop.

The parking lots at Mile High Stadium are empty now. A chill wind swirls scraps of litter against the chain link fence. No one is in the stadium. It waits patiently for future cheers.

Worshipers heap symbols upon ancient rituals and expect a miracle of joy. And for some, it works. There's nothing better than frankincense and myrrh. Unless maybe it's a stereo or a deluxe two-in-one toaster oven. And listen, there's a lot of good will and good cheer in just one more toddy for the road.

The road to Christmas is long. It seems to be just over there, under that star. Sometimes it seems so close, close enough to touch.

Is it Christmas when the child touches the bright star on the tree? Is it Christmas when the time runs out and the presents go unwrapped? Is it Christmas when the last drops of white port are gone from the bottle in the paper sack?

It is Christmas now.

The road doesn't end here. It starts here. It is the beginning. We start here, under this star. We find peace on Earth and high in a winter sky. There is good will in the smile of a stranger. We take gifts from the manger and the greatest of these is love.

The infant is life. We feel a special reverence for birth. The life we celebrate now is such a fragile, lovely thing. We have found our joy.

Joy to the world!

Rocky Mountain News columnist Gene Amole has had a long and varied career in radio and television in addition to his career as a newspaper journalist. He and a business partner started Denver Magazine *and also have operated several radio stations.*

Here Comes Santa!

by Gene Lindberg

At Christmastime we are not bound by laws of time & space.
No matter where we look we see an old, familiar face
That laughs at years and distances—and we laugh, too, because
We're glad to see the beard, the cheeks, the eyes of Santa Claus.

Where that face shines the miracle of Christmas can come true.
Old Santa doesn't count the miles as other trav'lers do.
In city crowds, on lonely plains; near, far and everywhere
We know because we see his face that Santa Claus is there.

We may not know the clothes he wears or recognize the steed
But Christmas gives us sight to know the doer by the deed.
Old Santa speeds around the world and nothing can disguise
The light of peace, goodwill toward men, that twinkles in his eyes.

Science writer for The Denver Post *for many years, Gene Lindberg also wrote the "jingles" that accompanied Paul Gregg's covers for* The Post's *Sunday magazine section.*

Christmas wasn't presents. It wasn't even talking about Christmas and singing Christmas songs. It was something that happened deep down in you, some happiness you had or those around you had.

Hal Borland, High, Wide and Lonesome

Of Myth and Merriment
by Marie Halun Bloch

Christmas for most adults is a brief return to innocence, and its meaning dwells in those customs and symbols that most of us share: the sudden fragrant aroma of pine that announces the advent, greeting cards with sparkles on them, the mysterious presence of the pagan tree decked with shiny, sparkly, tinsely things, the diamonds on a new snow in the moonlight, the magical eve—and family, family, family. A special simple kindness lies at the heart of Christmas.

These are the ingredients of Christmas, that abide beyond childhood. Of course they're cliches! But what of it? Cliche is the embryo of myth, and people that live by myth are healthier, happier and merrier!

Early in her career, Marie Halun Bloch was a regular contributor to The Washington Post *and has since authored more than 20 children's books.*

Will you make
my Christmas present
your heart?
You can wrap
it in yourself.

from Let's Share *by Alex English, a professional basketball player and poet.*

A Prayer For The Homeless
by Dr. Alan H. Landes

Gracious God of compassion and mercy: we lift up to you those women and men, boys and girls, who are this night without a place to call home. We pray for those who lay their heads on stones, who use paper bags for blankets, and who hope to find a breakfast to fill the empty place of no dinner. We pray for parents without work, worrying about their children sleeping in the back seat of their broken-down car. We pray for the homeless, the invisible people in need all around us.

In choosing to reveal your matchless glory in the bare poverty of a stable, you've chosen to identify yourself with the least of these among us. You know the rejection of being told that there is no room at the inn, being turned away and hearing the closing of doors to your human need.

This holiday season, open the floodgates of our hearts. Give meaning to our prayers by stimulating within us a door-opening generosity. God of hope, let the radiant glory of your love be born within us, that in Christ's name, we might become your Christmas gift to those around us. Amen.

Dr. Landes is pastor of Shepherd of The Hills Presbyterian Church in Lakewood, CO.

A·Holy·Happy·Christmas.

THE CHILDREN WERE NESTLED ALL SNUG IN THEIR BEDS

Christmas Through a Child's Eyes

Thrills of Delight

Miss Figg, the philanthropic president of the Ladies Relief Society, presented gifts to the poor children of Denver at her home, 447 Lawrence Street.

Little toys, books, puzzles, candles, fruits and clothes, sent thrills of delight to the hearts of the fifty-six waifs assembled at Miss Figg's rooms.

The Daily Rocky Mountain News, *1874*

"Toyland, Toyland, Beautiful Girl and Boy Land . . ."

It can be truthfully said that Denver has as fine a collection of toys on exhibition in its stores as any city in the United States. A visit to these stores well repay anyone who delights in seeing curiosities of all kinds and descriptions.

With the girls, dolls, it seems, will never be a back number . . . rag dolls, china dolls, wax dolls, bisque and rubber dolls . . . all are cheap and sell from 1 cent to $25. Another delight for the girl is the sewing machine. It is a wee small bit of a thing and can be purchased at a very reasonable price.

Hobby horses and rocking horses continue to be improved and Denver merchants say there has never been such a demand for them as there is this year . . . And every boy must have a tool chest in order that everything may be kept in good repair.

There is nothing more attractive to the child's eye than to see a toy that performs some feat. Among these that receive more than ordinary attention are the hummingbird, which when wound up will sing for an hour and a half; the shoemaker rabbit, who sews for about twenty minutes and never misses a stroke; the cat which is lying in a cradle, all the time kicking a rubber ball with its hand foot; the dancing Chinaman, who cuts up all kinds of capers; and a body of Rough Riders who go through the manual of arms.

Printing presses, pianos, music boxes, billiard tables and such articles are very popular this year. A gyrograph top is a new thing and is one of the best selling new articles yet placed on the market. It is wound up and set going and makes spiral figures, any of which would be a credit to a professor of penmanship.

Now that we have been favored with snow during the last week, sleds and skates have been sold in enormous quantities. Sleds range in price from 35 cents to $5.

In conclusion we must not forget the drums. While almost everyone agrees that the small boy makes an awful noise in case he secures one, still we must take into consideration the fact that this noise will only last a short time. The reason for this is that inside of two days the youth generally has pounded that instrument to pieces.

The Denver Times, *1899*

My Doll

by H. Eatches

You are almost as old as I, Dolly.
    You are twelve years old to-day,
And I am too old to play with dolls,
    At least so my sisters say.

I'll lay you away on a shelf so snug,
    You will close your eyes so blue,
And sleep all the coming years away.
    Oh, *how can* I part with you?

I suppose it will seem very strange to me
    To look at you, Dolly, dear,
And think you are nearly as old as I;
    Younger by only a year.

Some day when I am grown up, Dolly,
    Into a lady so tall,
So old that my dresses may touch my toes,
    So old I may go to a ball.

Now I'll lay you away to sleep, Dolly,
    Sleep the long years away,
For I'm too old to play with you, dear,
    At least, so my sisters say.

Crafts For An
Old Fashioned Christmas
Fingerprint Notepaper

Decorate notepaper with flowers and birds and animals you make from your own fingerprints.

You'll need: Stamp pad; felt pen with a fine tip; notepaper

Press your finger on the stamp pad and then on notepaper. By using fingers and thumb, and by rolling the finger, you can make a variety of shapes and sizes of prints.

● Now use your imagination to decorate the fingerprints. What do they look like? Pussy willows? Butterflies? Kittens? Use the felt pen to add stalks to pussy willows, stems to flowers, tail and ears to cats, or to outline butterfly wings.

● One-color designs are very attractive, but you can print notepaper in more than one color if you have stamp pads and pens in different colors.

Pebble Paperweight

Look for flat smooth stones about 1—1-1/2" long. If they're dark, paint them white; then paint on bright green Christmas trees.

● Glue decorated stones to inside of a large jar lid to make a paperweight. Glue a felt circle on bottom of paperweight. (This will cover printing on jar lid.)

Christmas Potpourri

5 cups
Mix and pour into little calico bags.

1 quart fir needles
1 cup dried, mixed fruit (without membranes), thinly shredded
1 cup rosemary
1/2 cup basil
2-4 bay leaves, coarsely crumbled
2 cups coarse salt (not iodized)

Colorado Cache Cookbook

The Clement Moore classic The Night Before Christmas, *published in newspapers in Colorado and nationwide in the 1860s, was originally composed for his children in 1822. Like Moore's poem the following stories by Mary Calhoun, Michael Gilbert, C.S. Bailey and Willa Cather, were created for family and friends. Like* A Night Before Christmas *they have the vibrancy of a story created with a special listener in mind.*

The Day Before Christmas Is Magic
by Mary Calhoun

The day before Christmas is a magical, waiting day. Maybe that's why the snowman was magic.

When Susan and Sam (here the reader may wish to substitute the names of immediate acquaintances known to make snowmen before Christmas) woke up the day before Christmas there was snow all over the ground and bushes.

"Oh, good!" cried Mother. "Snow for Christmas!"

"Let's build a snowman," said Susan.

Right after breakfast the two children put on their warmest clothing, and Susan helped Sam with his boots because she was bigger than he was.

The snow in the yard was clear and smooth and shining white. Not one track in it, not even a bird track. So, of course, Susan and Sam made tracks the first thing. Then they made angels by lying in the snow and moving their arms up and down.

Then they got busy on the snowman. First they started a big ball of snow, rolling it bigger and bigger. That was the bottom part of the snowman. Then they rolled up another big ball and set it on top of the first great ball. That was the snowman's chest. After that they made a very small ball for the snowman's head.

Sam ran to the basement for some little chunks of coal. One for each eye, one for the snowman's nose, and a smiling row of black coal chunks for the mouth. Susan stuck Daddy's oldest pipe into the coal mouth, then Sam plopped Daddy's fishing hat on the snowman's head.

"Now he's done," laughed Susan. "Let's go and get Mother to see."

"No, he's not ready," Sam said. "We haven't given him any ears or feet."

"Oh, silly," Susan laughed again. "Snowmen never have ears and feet. Nobody ever makes them that way."

"Well, our snowman is going to be better than other snowmen. He's going to have everything," Sam insisted as he stuck a lump of snow on each side of the snowman's head, for ears.

Then Sam ran back into the house and brought out an old pair of Daddy's boots. He fixed the boots just right at the bottom of the snowman, for the feet.

Neighbor children came over to see the snowman. As they played in the snow with Susan and Sam, the boys and girls talking about Christmas and Santa Claus and the North Pole. Mostly they talked about what they wanted Santa Claus to bring them for Christmas.

And the snowman heard every word. Because of his ears, of course.

Some other children started to slide with their sleds on the hill by the house. So Susan and Sam and their friends ran off to get their sleds, leaving the snowman alone.

All day the snowman watched the children sliding on their sleds. It looked like so much fun. By nightfall the snowman knew what *he* wanted for Christmas—a sled! He could just see himself taking a run—*ker whump*—falling on the sled, and sailing down the hill.

As it started to darken into Christmas Eve, the children went into their houses. When Susan and Sam went in, the snowman heard them talking about hanging up their stockings so that Santa Claus could fill them with presents. He saw the chimney on the house, where Santa Claus would slide down. Through the window the snowman could see the children's Christmas tree, already lit.

Poor snowman. He didn't have any stocking to hang up, or any Christmas tree. He had no chimney for Santa Claus to slide down.

"But I *do* have feet!" the snowman said to himself. "I can walk to the North Pole and ask Santa Claus for a sled for Christmas."

So the snowman started walking, there in the early darkness. Right through the front gate and off down the street. He could walk because *he* had feet. Or maybe because Christmas is such a magical time. Anyway the snowman kept right on walking.

He didn't know which way to go to reach the North Pole. But he saw a sign that said, "North High Street." The children had mentioned the North Pole, so North High Street must be the way to Santa Claus' house, the snowman decided.

Clump, clump, clump, the snowman walked on out North High Street until he came to the edge of the town. Across the field he saw a little house with a light in the window. "That must be Santa Claus' house," the snowman thought.

He hurried across the snowy field and knocked at the door. An old man with a bushy white beard opened the door and peered out. He looked just the way the children had said, so the snowman was sure he had found Santa Claus.

"Please, Santa, may I have a sled for Christmas? I know it's late to be asking. But I came here to ask because I don't have any stocking to hang up, and I don't have a Christmas tree for you to leave the sled under, or a house where you could come down the chimney."

The old man was surprised. And the reason he felt surprised was because he wasn't Santa Claus at all! The snowman did not know that the North Pole is a lot farther away than the edge of town.

But the old man knew that magic things can happen on Christmas Eve. So he led the snowman around to the back of his house and showed him a sled that was leaning against a tree.

"There's your sled. Take it now, and have fun with it," he said.

The snowman thanked the old man and dragged the sled to a hill back of the house. And there, all night long, the snowman slid on his sled—run, *flop*, wheee!—and clumped back up again.

At last, when the light of Christmas morning began to brighten the snow, the snowman was worn out. He stopped under a tree near the old man's back door and sat down on the sled to take a rest.

Tired and happy, the snowman was soon fast asleep. The morning sun came up and shone bright and warm. The snow on the trees and bushes began to melt and drip to the ground. The snow on the ground was warmed by the sun and began to melt away. As for the snowman, who was asleep on his sled—he, too, began to melt in the sun.

Susan and Sam didn't miss the snowman, for they were busy with Christmas. But when the old man came out that morning he found the sled under the tree. And all that was left besides that were the boots next to the sled, the hat and pipe, and on the sled, the chunks of coal that were the snowman's smile.

Author of numerous children's books, Mary Calhoun lives in Steamboat Springs. Her *Cross-Country Cat* was recently published in the People's Republic of China.

A Caterpillar Christmas

by Michael Gilbert

All the caterpillars were growing wide stripes. Brilliant colors filled the woods. Even the ants could see their breath. Winter was coming.

Willie was a wooly-bear caterpillar whose body was covered with orange and black fuzz. He loved crawling around on the tree branches. He'd get out on the skinny limbs and look down, but he was never scared because he hung on with lots of little feet.

Now Willie was a very curious caterpillar. He wanted to know about everything. He wanted to know what snow tasted like, if he could skate on the frost, and mostly he wanted to know about Santa Claus. Everyone said, "No one ever *sees* Santa Claus. He comes out really late at night when everyone's asleep."

"Not me," said Willie.

His mom and dad said, "Willie, you have to be asleep. Caterpillars make cocoons. That's what keeps them warm through the winter so they won't freeze!"

"I don't care," said Willie, "I want to see Santa Claus."

The caterpillar kids on the upstairs branch were having a slumber party, each one spinning a small sleeping bag. Willie didn't want to make a sleeping bag. He wasn't tired. He wanted to watch it snow, and mostly he wanted to meet Santa Claus.

All week long caterpillars were finding sticks to hang their cocoons from, but not Willie. He was busy piling up leaves and jumping in. He crawled into a curled gold aspen leaf to see if it felt warmer than the brown oaks.

"Good," said everyone, "Willie has finally found a place to sleep, "Surprise!" yelled Willie, wiggling out the other side.

"Oh No!" they all groaned.

Willie heard a marching song.

"The ants go marching one by one . . ."

A whole line of ants marched past him carrying food.

"Hey, where are you guys going?"

The ants just kept marching, so Willie picked up a leaf and started crunching, following right along behind. One by one they disappeared down their hole until Willie was left at the top looking down. "Can I come down too?" he asked.

"No, you're too big. Go away. We're busy."

"What are you doing down there anyway?"

We're storing our food where it's warm and dry because winter's coming. When it's all snowy and cold out there, we'll be down here having a party."

"You'll miss Santa Claus!"

But they were too deep into their hole to hear him.

Willie climbed back into his tree and decided to try skydiving with a big red maple leaf. He held on with all his feet and jumped into thin air from the top branch. "I can fly!" he called to the slumber party, as he sailed past.

"We're trying to sleep!" they yelled, "Fly somewhere else!"

He drifted to the ground and spent the rest of the day playing hide-and-seek by himself under piles of leaves. In the morning when he peeked out, he found everything covered with fuzzy white frost. Maybe this is snow, he thought, and climbed into his old tree for a better look. All his family and friends were curled in their cocoons, fast asleep.

"Oh boy, now they'll leave me alone. I can wait for winter and watch for Santa and make all the noise I want! Yipee!"

The leaves had all blown away in the night and Willie could see clear across the field. Santa's house must be just on the other side of that hill he thought. Now he could see everything, but everything could also see him, including a big blue jay. The bird swooped down toward his branch. Willies' little legs ran as fast as they could go and he jumped into a squirrel hole.

"Willie!" cried the squirrel. "What are you doing out so late? Does your mother know you're up?"

"I'm staying up for winter and Santa Claus. Does he come pretty soon?"

"I don't know and I don't care," scolded the squirrel, "But you can't wait in here. I need all this room for my nuts. Get out of here!"

What a grouch! thought Willie, but the bird had flown away, so he crawled back out on the branch and tried to hide behind one last leaf, but now all the leaves were gone. He began feeling scared. He needed a place to hide, a place where he could see, but nothing could see him. All the trees and bushes were bare except for a small green one next to the house on the hill. It was as furry as he was. "Maybe I could hide in there," said Willie and he inched down, through the leaves on the ground toward the tree.

The evergreen was a perfect hiding place. He snuggled down in a piney bough to rest after his long trip.

Something shook the tree and he woke up. He must have been asleep for a long time because he noticed it was much colder and white stuff was coming out of the sky . . . Maybe I *should* make a cocoon, he thought, but he STILL wanted to see Santa. The white stuff was clinging to his fuzzy fur and he stuck out his tongue to taste it. It was COLD and HE was cold. I hope Santa gets here pretty soon, he shivered. The tree shook again and a large hand passed in front of his face, leaving a string of strange colored berries. The berries were red and blue and green. Maybe they're good to eat, he thought, crawling up to the red one. He opened his mouth to bite it when it started to glow. It was WARM next to the red "berry" and he warmed up all his feet. Willie heard people's voices. "What a pretty Christmas tree!" Do you think Santa will see it tonight?"

Oh boy, thought Willie, Christmas must be close.

All day the snow piled up and Willie stayed close to the bulb. It grew darker and darker. He was yawning when suddenly he heard sleigh bells. They came closer and closer and then . . .

"HO, HO, HO, what's this? Someone is still up!" A big red mitten reached down and picked Willie up. "Willie, where's your cocoon?" said Santa. Willie just stared with his mouth and eyes wide open. "Willie, everyone has to be asleep on Christmas. Have you been a good caterpillar this year?"

Willie tried to speak but his head just nodded up and down.

"Well OK, let's see what I might have in here for a cater-pillar." He reached into his big bag and pulled out a video game. "No, this won't go." He put it back and came up with a Barbie Doll. "No still too big," he said, and dug way down in the bottom. "HO, HO, HO!" he laughed and pulled out a stocking, just big enough for Willie.

Willie wiggled in backwards until all that was showing were his two sleepy eyes and a big caterpillar yawn. Santa hung him back on the tree, patted his head and said, "This is how caterpillars should spend Christmas." Willie snuggled down in his sock with a warm glow inside and fell fast asleep.

Mike Gilbert is a former teacher-turned-storymaker who creates stories with audiences of all ages. He lives in the Colorado foothills in a seventy-year-old log cabin with his wife-teacher-friend Caroline. He has a pet caterpillar named Buzghetti.

SANTA CLAUS

SANTA CLAUS PLEASE COME ON DOWN
I WANT TO FLY WITH YOU
IN YOUR SLED ALL BUNDLED WITH TOYS
PLEASE LET ME BE WITH YOU
UP SO HIGH IN WONDERLAND SKY
COUNTING THE STARS GO BY
SEE THE REINDEER SIX, SEVEN, EIGHT
OH, DEAR SANTA, I CAN'T WAIT

LET ME COME TO SANTA CLAUS LAND
I COULD BE YOUR FRIEND
HELP YOU MAKE THOSE BEAUTIFUL TOYS
AND ASK MY MOM TO SEND YOU
COOKIES AND CANDIES, PUDDINGS AND CAKES
CHERRIES AND APPLES TOO
WE COULD HAVE SUCH JOLLY FUN
JUST US TWO AND MRS. SANTA

HEAR ME, SANTA, IF I CAN'T COME
TO LIVE WITH YOU IN YOUR HOUSE
BRING ME TOYS, PLEASE, LOTS IF YOU CAN
ESPECIALLY A REAL LIVE MOUSE
TRUCKS RED OR YELLOW, I REALLY DON'T CARE
BOATS OR A PLANE WOULD DO
I LIKE TRAINS, A CIRCUS TRAIN
WITH ANIMALS FROM THE ZOO

SANTA CLAUS, I PROMISE TO BE
THANKFUL AND GOOD AND KIND
HELP MY MOMMY PICK UP MY CLOTHES
BRUSH EVERY TOOTH, SHARE WITH MY FRIENDS
NOT SIT ON THE CAT, NOT WATER THE RUG,
NOT SQUISH LITTLE BUGS. . . .
OH, SANTA, I LOVE YOU.

From the album "I Love Life" by Aspen Songwriter Laurie Lozac'h.

by Jamie White

The Tree That Trimmed Itself

by Carolyn Sherwin Bailey

"I wish, oh, how I wish!" sighed the young Pine Tree, as Christmas wind blew through its branches, "that I might be a Christmas Tree with decorations like my brother who was cut down!"

The forest was very still and cold. It was Christmas Eve, the season of wonder, but very few trees had been cut for the children. So many tall, strong ones would be needed for building homes and for kindling fires and for making furniture. But, oh, the happiness of a Christmas tree sparkling in the light of the home fire, with a circle of happy children dancing about it! No wonder that the young Pine Tree sighed again in the wind.

"I wish that I might be trimmed for Christmas!" it whispered.

Suddenly something happened there in the woods. Floating down among the outspread branches of the Pine Tree came white stars, shaped like shining crystals.

More and then still more snow stars fell, until every twig of every branch of the tree held its white star.

They were more beautiful than any ornaments that the toyman had for trimming a Christmas Tree.

But still the young Pine Tree longed for all the honors his brother tree would have. "I wish that I might hear the Christmas chimes!" it sighed in the wind.

Then the night grew colder and colder. The frost came through the forest and stopped beside the Pine Tree, hanging sharp, hard icicles to the tips of the twigs.

Whenever the wind touched the tree the icicles tinkled and rang like a chime of tiny Christmas bells. They made soft, beautiful Christmas music.

But still the young Pine Tree was not satisfied. "I wish," it sighed, "that I might hold lights as my brother will on this Christmas Eve."

Suddenly the stars shone out in the darkness and dropped their beams of light down as far as the branches of the young Pine Tree. One star seemed to leave the sky and rest on the topmost twig of the Pine Tree. There it flamed and flashed like a beacon to call everyone to see the wonders of Christmas Eve. The Pine Tree was lighted as brightly as if it carried a hundred candles, but still it had a wish.

"I am still not yet a Christmas Tree!" it sighed. "I wish that I might hold gifts among my branches." And it seemed as this wish could never come true, for where could Christmas gifts be found in the wintry forest?

Christmas Eve changed to the very early dawning of Christmas Day. Still the Pine Tree wore its snow stars. Its icicle chimes rang in the clear, cold air, and the light of the sky shone in its branches like a Christmas light. And out from the shelter of a nest among its roots crept a tiny mouse, cold and hungry.

How nice! Hanging to the Pine Tree, just above the nest of the mouse, was a bunch of berries and its trailing vine.

The vine had twisted itself around the trunk of the Tree in the summertime and now, in the deep winter, its bright berries hung there, a gift on Christmas morning for the hungry little mouse.

And out from the shelter of the trunk of the Pine Tree came a squirrel. He, too, was hungry. But he scampered along the branch until he came to the part of the Tree where it had held tightly, in spite of the winter gales, a fat, brown cone.

The squirrel held the cone daintily in his paws, cut out the seeds and munched them.

It was his holiday breakfast and how good it tasted! No better Christmas gift could have come to the squirrel than that fat pine cone so full of seeds.

"Merry Christmas!" called the children, running to the woods later on the morning of Christmas Day. "Merry Christmas, little Pine Tree. We have brought a gift for your snow bird. We heard him calling yesterday."

In their red caps and mittens, the happy children came dancing through the woods with a bundle of ripe grain.

They reached up as far as they could and hung it by a gay red ribbon to one of the green branches of the little Pine Tree. Then they exclaimed, and they stood farther back in the path, for the snow bird came out from an empty nest among the branches which grew thickest to feast on the grain.

"The snow bird rested in a cradle on Christmas Eve!" The children said to each other. "The little Pine Tree must have held that empty nest very closely all winter to give the snow bird a Christmas cradle!"

And the little Pine Tree stood straight and happy there in the woods on Christmas morning, for all of its wishes had come true It had trimmed itself with stars and heard the chimes and had offered its gifts to its little neighbors of the forest. And still it could grow for the building of homes when it was an older, larger pine!

The Year Santa Came Late
by Willa Cather

This is a tale of the bleak, bitter Northland, where the frost is eternal and the snows never melt, where the wide white plains stretch for miles and miles . . . and where the Heavens at night are made terribly beautiful by the trembling flashes of the northern lights, and the green icebergs float in stately grandeur down the dark currents of the hungry polar sea. . . . The only cheerful thing about all this country is that far up within the Arctic Circle, just on the edge of the boundless snow plains, there is a big house . . . where lights shine all year round from the windows, and the wide halls are warmed by blazing fires. For this is the house of his beloved Saintship, Nicholas, whom the children the world over call Santa Claus.

Now every child knows this house is beautiful, and beautiful it is, for it is one of the most home-like places in the world. Just inside the front door is the big hall, where every evening after his work is done Santa Claus sits by the roaring fire and chats with his wife, Mamma Santa, and the White Bear. Then there is the dining room, and the room where Papa and Momma Santa sleep, and to the rear are the workshops, where all the wonderful toys are made, and last of all the White Bear's sleeping room, for the White Bear has to sleep in a bed of clean white snow every night, and so his room is away from the heated part of the house.

But most boys and girls do not know much about the White Bear, for though he is really a very important personage, he has been strangely neglected by the biographers of Santa Claus. . . . He is not at all like the bears who carry off naughty children, and does not even belong to the same family as the bears who ate up the forty children who mocked at the Prophet's bald head. On the contrary, this bear is a most gentle and kindly fellow, and fonder of boys and girls than any one else in the world, except Santa Claus himself. He has lived with Papa Santa from time immemorial, helping him in his workshop, painting rocking horses, and stretching drum heads, and gluing yellow wigs on doll babies. But his principal duty is to care for the reindeer, those swift, strong, nervous little beasts, without whom the hobby horses and dolls and red drums would never reach the little children in the world.

One evening, on the twenty-third of December—the rest of the date does not matter—Papa Santa sat by the fire in the great hall, blowing the smoke from his nostrils, until his ruddy round face shone through it like a full moon through the mist. He was in a happier mood even than usual, for his long year's work in his shop was done, the last nail had been driven, the last coat of paint had dried. All the vast array of toys stood ready to go into the sealskin bags and be piled into the sleigh for the children of the world.

Opposite him sat Mamma Santa, putting the last dainty stitches on a doll dress for a little sick girl somewhere down in the world. Mamma Santa never kept track of where the different children lived; Papa Santa and the White Bear attended to the address book. It was enough for her to know that they were children and good children, she didn't care to know any more. By her chair sat the White Bear, eating his dog sausage. The White Bear was always hungry between meals, and Mamma Santa always kept a plate of his favorite sausage ready for him in the pantry, which, as there was no fire there, was a refrigerator as well.

As Papa Santa bent to light his pipe once again, he spoke to the White Bear:

"The reindeer are all in good shape, are they? You've seen them tonight? There are no problems?"

"I gave them their feed and rubbed them down an hour ago, and I never saw them friskier. They ought to skim like birds tomorrow night. As I came away, though, I thought I saw the Were-Wolf Dog hanging around, so I locked up the stable."

"That was right," said Papa Santa, approvingly. "He was there for no good, depend on that. Last year he tampered with the harness and cut it so that four traces broke before I reached Norway."

Mamma Santa sent her needle through the fine cambric she was stitching with an indignant thrust, and spoke so emphatically that the little white curls under her cap bobbed about her face. "I cannot understand the perverse wickedness of that animal, nor what he has against you, that he should be forever troubling you, or against those World-Children, poor little innocents, that he should be forever trying to defraud them of their Christmas presents. He is certainly the meanest animal from here to the Pole."

"That he is," said Papa Santa, "and there is no reason for it at all. But he hates everything that is not mean as himself."

"I am sure, Papa, that he will never be at rest until he has brought about some serious accident. Hadn't the Bear better look about the stables again?"

"I'll sleep there tonight and watch, if you say so," said the White Bear, rapping the floor with his shaggy tail.

"O, there is no need of that, we must all get our sleep tonight, for we have hard work and a long journey before us tomorrow. I can trust the reindeer pretty well to look after themselves. Come, Mamma, come, we must get to bed." Papa Santa shook the ashes out of his pipe and blew out the lights, and the White Bear went to stretch himself in his clean white snow.

When all was quiet about the house, there stole from out the shadow of the wall a great dog, shaggy and monstrous to look upon. His hair was red, and his eyes were bright, like ominous fires. . . . and there was always a little foam about his lips as though he were raging with some inward fury. He carried his tail between his legs, for he was a cowardly as he was vicious. This was the wicked Were-

Wolf Dog who hated everything; the beasts and the birds and Santa Claus and the White Bear, and most of all the little children of the world. Nothing made him so angry as to think that there really are good children in the world, little children who love each other, and are simple and gentle and fond of everything that lives, whether it breathes or blooms. For years he had been trying in one way and another to delay Santa Claus' journey so that the children would get no beautiful gifts from him at Christmastime. For the Were-Wolf Dog hated Christmas too, incomprehensible as that may seem. He was thoroughly wicked and evil, and Christmas time is the birth-day of Goodness, and every year on Christmas Eve the rage in his dark heart burned anew.

He stole softly to the window of the stable, and peered in where the swift, tiny reindeer stood each in his warm little stall, pawing the ground impatiently. For on glorious moonlight nights like that the reindeer never slept, they were always so homesick for their free-dom and their wide white snow plains.

"Little reindeer," called the Were-Wolf Dog, softly, and all the little reindeer pricked up their ears, "Little reindeer, it is a lovely night," and all the little reindeer sighed softly. They knew, ah, how well they knew!

"Little reindeer, the moon is shining as brightly as the sun does in the summer; the North wind is blowing fresh and cold, driving the little clouds across the sky like white sea birds. The snow is just hard enough to bear without breaking, and your brothers are running like wild things over its white crust. And the stars, ah, the stars, little brothers, they gleam like a million jewels, and glitter like icicles all over the face of the sky. Come, see how they sparkle."

The reindeer stamped impatiently in their little stalls. It was very hard. They wanted to be out racing freely with all the other reindeer.

"Come, little reindeer, let me tell you why all your brothers run toward the Polar Sea tonight. It is because tonight the northern lights will flash as they never did before, and the great streaks of red and purple and violet will shoot across the sky until all the people of the world shall see them, who never saw before. Listen, little rein-deer, it is just the night for a run, a long free run, with no traces to tangle your feet and no sleigh to drag. Come, let us go, you will be back again by dawn and no one will ever know."

Dunder stamped in his stall, it made him long to be gone, to hear what the Were-Wolf Dog said. "No, no, we cannot, for tomorrow we must start with the toys for the little children of the world."

"But you will be back tomorrow. Just when the dim light is touching the tops of the icebergs and making the fresh snow red, you will be speeding home. Ah, it will be a glorious run, and you will see the lights as they never shone before. Do you not pant to feel the wind about you, little reindeer?"

Then Cupid and Blitzen could withstand his enticing words no longer, and begged, "Come, Dunder, let us go tonight. It has been so long since we have seen the lights, and we will be back tomorrow."

Now the reindeer knew well enough they ought not to go, but reindeer are not like people, and sometimes the things they want most awfully to do are the very things that they ought not to do. The thought of the fresh winds and their dear lights of the North and the moonlight snow drove them wild, for the reindeer love their freedom more than any other animal, and swift motion, and the free winds.

So the dog pried open the door, with the help of the reindeer forcing it from within, and they all dashed out into the clear moonlight and scurried away toward the North like gleeful rabbits. "We will be back by morning," said Cupid. "We will be back," said Dunder. And, poor little reindeer, they loved the snow so well that it scarcely seemed wrong to go.

O, how fine it was to feel that wind in their fur again! They tossed their antlers in the fresh wind, and their tiny hoofs rang on the hard snow as they ran. They ran for miles and miles without growing tired, or losing their first pleasure in it. . . .

"Slower, slower, little reindeer, for I must lead the way. You will not find the place where the beasts are assembled," called the Were-Wolf Dog.

The little reindeer could no more go slowly than a boy can when the fire engines dash by. So they got the Were-Wolf Dog in the center of the pack and fairly bore him on with them. On they ran over those vast plains of snow that sparkled as brightly as the sky did above, and Dasher and Prancer bellowed aloud with glee. At last there lay before them the boundless stretch of the Polar Sea.

Dark and silent it was, as mysterious as the strange secret of the Pole which it guards forever. Here and there where the ice floes had parted showed a crevice of black water, and the great walls of ice glittered like flame when the northern lights flung their red banners across the sky, and tipped the icebergs with fire. There the reindeer paused a moment for very joy, and the Were-Wolf Dog fell behind silently.

"Is the ice safe, old dog?" asked Vixen, calling to the Were-Wolf Dog.

"To the right it is, off and away, little reindeer. It is growing late," said the Were-Wolf Dog, shouting hoarsely; "To the right."

And the heedless little reindeer dashed on, never noticing that the wicked Were-Wolf Dog stayed behind on the shore. Now when they were out a good way upon the sea they heard a frightful cracking grinding sound, such as the ice makes when it breaks up.

"To the shore, little brothers, to the shore!" cried Dunder, but it was too late. The wicked Were-Wolf Dog where he stood on the land saw the treacherous ice break and part, and the head of every little reindeer go down under the black water. Then he turned and fled over the snow, with his tail tighter between his legs than ever, for he was too cowardly to look upon his own evil work.

As for the reindeer, the black current caught them and whirled them down under the ice, all but Dunder and Dasher and Prancer, who at last rose to the surface and lifted their heads above the water.

"Swim, little brothers, we may yet make the shore," cried Dunder. So among the cakes of broken ice that cut them at every stroke, the three brave little beasts began to struggle toward the shore that seemed so far away. A great chunk of ice struck Prancer in the breast, and he groaned and sank. Then Dasher began to breathe heavily and fell behind, and when Dunder stayed to help him he said, "No, no, little brother, I cannot make it. You must not try to help me, or we will both go down. Go tell it all to the White Bear. Goodbye, little brother, we will skim the white snow fields no more together." And with that he, too, sank down into the black water, and Dunder struggled on all alone.

When at last he dragged himself wearily upon the shore he was exhausted and cruelly cut and bleeding. But there was no time to be lost. Spent and suffering as he was, he set out across the plains.

Late in the night the White Bear heard someone tapping, tapping against his window and saw poor Dunder standing there all covered with ice and blood.

"Come out, brother," he gasped, "the others are all dead and drowned, only I am left. . . ."

Then the White Bear hastened out . . . and Dunder told him all about the cruel treachery of the Were-Wolf Dog.

"Alas," cried the White Bear," and who shall tell Santa of this, and who will drag his sleigh tomorrow to carry the gifts to the little children of the world? Empty will their stockings hang on Christmas morning, and Santa's heart will be broken."

Then poor Dunder sank down in the snow and wept.

"Do not despair, Dunder. We must go tonight to the ice hummock where the beasts meet to begin their Christmas revels. Can you run a little longer, poor reindeer?"

"I will run until I die," said Dunder, bravely. "Get on my back and we will go." . . . And they sped away to the great ice hummock where the animals of the North all gather to keep their Christmas.

The ice hummock is a great pile of ice and snow right under the North Star, and all the animals were there drinking punches and wishing each other a Merry Christmas. There were seals, and fur otters, and white ermines, and whales, and bears, and many strange birds, and the tawny Lapland dogs that are as strong as horses. But the Were-Wolf Dog was not there. The White Bear paid no heed to any of them, but climbed up to the very top of the huge ice hummock. Then he stood up and cried out:

"Animals of the North, listen to me!" and all the animals ceased from their merrymaking and looked up to the ice hummock where the White Bear stood, looking very strange up there, all alone in the starlight.

"Listen to me," thundered the White Bear," and I will tell you such a tale of wickedness and treachery as never came up among us before. This night the wicked Were-Wolf Dog . . . came to the reindeer of Santa Claus and with enticing words lured them northward, promising to show them the great lights as they never shone before. But black Death he showed them, and the bottom of the Polar Sea." Then he showed them poor bleeding Dunder, and told how all the tiny reindeer had been drowned and all the treachery of the Were-Wolf Dog. . . .

"Now, O animals," the White Bear went on, "who among you will go back with me and draw the sleigh full of presents down to the little World-Children, for a shame would it be to all of us if they should awaken and find themselves forgotten and their stockings empty."

But none of the animals replied . . .

"What," cried the White Bear. "Is there not one of you who will . . . take the place of our brothers who are now dead? . . ."

But the animals all thought of the wide plains and the stinging North wind and their scampers of old, and hung their heads and were silent. Poor Dunder groaned aloud, and even the White Bear had begun to despair, when there spoke up a poor old seal with but one fin, for he had fallen into the seal fishers' hands and been maimed. . . . "I am only an old seal who has been twice wounded by the hunters, and am a cripple, but lo, I myself will go with the White Bear, and though I can travel but a mile a day at best, yet will I hobble on my tail and my one fin until I have dragged the sleigh full of presents to the World-Children."

Then the animals were all ashamed of themselves, and the reindeer all sprang forward and cried, "We will go, take us!"

So the next day, a little later than usual, Santa Claus wrapped himself in his fur lap robes, and seven new reindeer, headed by Dunder, flew like the winged wind toward the coast of Norway. And if any of you remember getting your presents a little late that year, it was because the new reindeer were not used to their work yet, though they tried hard enough.

One of the best known American writers of this century, Willa Cather was born in Virginia and migrated westward with her family when she was nine. Many of her short stories and novels are set in the small towns and rugged frontier of Nebraska, New Mexico and Colorado.

CUTTING CHRISTMAS TREES.

I'LL BE HOME FOR CHRISTMAS

Cherishing the Memories

Bough Gathering Time
by Enid Slack

EVERY December in Colorado at bough-gathering time I remember almost with melancholy a Christmas spent in England. I was about 24, young and a long way from home. I was invited to a tiny old village in Hartsfordshire, about 50 miles from London, where friends of mine lived in a 16th-century manor house. In the Great Room, next to a wide window with hand-blown glasspanes, stood a 12-foot blue spruce decorated with handmade straw stars, shiny apples and polished walnuts. When Paul, my host, lit the candles with a taper, the flickering light set off the old hues of the oak paneling and made the enormous room intimate with mystery any fire.

In the early evening, as they had for generations, Aston church bells rang, calling the villagers to a service. Paul urged me to accompany him to the front door. I wondered why, but followed. We stepped outside. Here the ringing of the bells was more distinct—so clear and plain that it made me ache inside with sadness.

Paul raised his long arm, pointed his finger toward the church and said in a husky voice, "Listen, Enid, listen. The bells. That, my dear, is the Christmas sound of England."

Here in Colorado, Christmas feels so different; there's a spaciousness here that is unique. The high peaks of Colorado tell their own story. Their starkness burns me. Here I look through the trees to the other side of the world. I'm scared. I'm excited.

57

As I wake this Christmas morning I see lodgepole pine covered with snow so fine it could have been sifted by a fairy. Last night beneath a sky that seemed so endless with stars I thought I saw the other side of space.

Enid Slack is a Denver-based writer. She directs national public relations projects, has written for USA Today *and contributes to* Colorado Homes & Lifestyles. *She is a recipient of a fellowship from the Rocky Mountain Women's Institute.*

Nature's Gift

by Gudy Gaskill

We moved back to Colorado in 1958 following a two-year stay in California. We ended up putting all our money into a cozy old house in the Lookout Mountain area. It had a faulty roof and a few other things wrong with it, but we were drawn to the natural setting and the privacy. By October the house was ready and we moved in with our children Steve, six years old, and Robin, eight.

The rustic setting wasn't complete until we rigged up a place for the birds and animals to come to feed. We used an old door, setting it on some rocks and logs. Many birds, neighborhood skunks and squirrels shared the scraps we put out for them.

One day we were stunned—a cardinal came to feed with the other creatures. Cardinals are not native to Colorado so we felt honored to have one right in our backyard. Friends, some from the Audubon Society, and neighbors came from all around to observe and marvel at this bird of brilliant hue. He showed up every day without fail, around seven in the morning and again in the afternoon at five.

In late November the snow started to fall and our special guest stopped coming.

Christmas was approaching and we didn't have much money to spend on gifts. Our children said the only thing they wanted for Christmas was the cardinal. They wished for it to come back and checked the feeder every day for a show of red feathers. Their sad eyes relayed a message of disappointment as each feeding time passed.

A few days before Christmas it started to snow really hard. The snow piled up and we fashioned a scoop out of some wood to push the heavy stuff off our already sagging roof. It snowed and snowed and the children watched and waited. They came up with the idea to put out a Christmas present for the cardinal. Trimming fat from their meat at suppertime, they carefully set the pieces on the door-feeder, outlining the edges. They watched for hours from the kitchen window, hoping their Christmas treat of suet would bring back their special friend.

It snowed all through Christmas Eve and as the children went to bed that night, our hearts were heavy, thinking that the cardinal was probably dead.

On Christmas morning we got up and looked out to see that the snow had stopped. The deep drifts gleamed in the bright sun and we sat down to a simple breakfast. The children glanced hopefully at the feeder which we had kept cleared of snow. They saw only a swarm of yellow-breasted grosbeaks feeding on the Christmas suet.

Then it happened. The cardinal appeared. At nine that morning he flew in and perched there with the feisty grosbeaks, who usually chased all other birds away. It was remarkable that they all feasted there together, enjoying the children's gift. The Christmas visitor returned to the feeder several times that day, fulfilling our children's dreams.

When the grandparents called to ask the children what they got for presents, Steve said, "Santa brought us the Cardinal." He would tell them of nothing else.

As the days following Christmas turned into the new year, the cardinal never returned. But the image of the majestic red bird against the drifted white snow of Christmas Day will stay in our memories forever.

Gudy Gaskill is founder and president of the Colorado Trail Foundation. Her work was honored with the Pride in America Award in 1987 and was featured in a 1989 Family Circle magazine series on "Women Who Make A Difference." She has received recognition from Presidents Reagan and Bush.

The Lionel Express
by Clive Cussler

Christmas 1938 did not begin on a high note. A few weeks before the holidays I entered the hospital with an advanced case of pneumonia, an all too common ailment of children who hiked to school through sub-zero weather and deep snowdrifts. Those were the days before penicillin and antibiotics. They put you in an oxygen tent and hoped for the best.

My parents were fond of reporting in later years that I came within an inch of drifting into the great beyond. They claimed the doctors were not optimistic until the fever broke. That part of the crisis is lost to me, but I vividly recall the good part, the days of getting better.

While I was sitting in bed one morning the police brought in a poor drunken derelict they'd found freezing in an alley. The nurses put him in the bed next to mine and began working to restore his vital signs. His name was Wendell, and when he revived we became pals.

He took pity on the pale, frail kid who was his ward mate, regaling me with stories my child-mind has long since forgotten. He made incredibly funny faces. The hours passed without that awful cough coming from deep inside me as I listened to Wendell's tales. I remember how he'd tear out magazine pages and fold them into all sorts of creative animals. I was fascinated when he did outlandish tricks with his false teeth. I was happier than I had been in days, and Wendell's antics soon made me forget my problems.

The following morning the nurse entered our two bed ward and asked me how I was feeling. I told her I was fine, but suggested she should ask old Wendell how he felt since he hadn't come awake yet and his skin seemed to have turned an unhealthy color.

The nurse gasped and quickly swept the curtains around Wendell's bed. Then the orderlies rushed in and laid him on a stretcher. Unfortunately, they were too late. My father entered the room just as they were pushing Wendell's sheet-covered body to the morgue.

Now you have to understand, my father was an excitable man. No complaint was made in a timid tone. He was an old German used to getting his way. I can still hear his accented voice hurtling up and down the corridor outside my room as he ripped into the hospital staff for allowing a "street bum" to die next to a six-year-old boy who had just been snatched back from the jaws of death.

Against heated protest from the doctors and nurses, he bundled me up and took me home, figuring I could better recuperate in my own room, away from the unfeeling hospital staff. The Depression was still lingering, and I suspect that saving a few days of hospital costs also had bearing on my father's decision.

Christmas Eve came two nights later, and I fell asleep, happy to be back in my own bed at home. I woke up once in the darkness and heard a combination of strange sounds. A "clickity click" accompanied by a whirring sound drifted into my room. I wondered if it was Santa Claus. But still weak and barely able to walk, I lacked the strength to climb from bed and make it into the living room to find out.

Morning came and Mother and Dad helped me into a robe and half carried me into the living room. Leaning on them for support, I stared in awe at what had to be the finest, fastest, shiniest electric train ever given to a six-year-old. A Lionel Express o gauge gray locomotive, complete with a tender and three bright red passenger cars, raced around the Christmas tree, headlights beaming, over an oblong track that seemed to take up half the living room. There was also a paper mache tunnel painted like a mountain and a little white house where a tiny man in blue uniform would snap out a door and raise his lantern as the train sped past.

How my father had scraped up the twenty-five dollars—a princely sum in 1938—to buy such a stupendous layout is still a mystery to me.

I lay on the floor for a long time, entranced with the lantern swinger. I watched the door whip open as the blue uniformed figure jumped from his house, swung the lantern and popped inside again.

My mother, watching me, noted my interest. "Why don't you give him a name?" she asked.

I thought for a moment and then nodded. "I'm going to call him Wendell."

"That's an odd name. Where did you get it?"

I continued to gaze at the little lantern swinger as I replied, "From a man who makes funny faces."

Author of many best-sellers, Clive Cussler divides his time between Golden Colorado, and Scottsdale, Arizona. "The Lionel Express" appears here in print for the first time.

Snow Soldiers at Christmas Time

The U.S. Army 10th Mountain Division trained fourteen thousand soldiers in ski and outdoor survival techniques during the winters of 1942 to 1944 at Camp Hale, Colorado. In the mountainous encampment which became a catalyst for the future development of many Colorado ski resorts, the soldiers managed to fit Christmas into their rigorous training schedule.

A conspicuous "first" will hit the airwaves Sunday morning at 10 o'clock over Denver's KOA when "Camp Hale Story" features the first presentation in America of the true story behind the famous Christmas Carol, "Silent Night."

This unique broadcast will describe in a dramatic manner how Father Mohr, priest of the village of Oberndorf, Austria, and Franz Gruber, wrote and composed the hymn in 1818.

The broadcast story is at variance in many points with the accepted versions of how "Silent Night" was written, but authenticity is added to the Camp Hale broadcast version by Pvt. Hannes Kohr, a native of Oberndorf and one of the writers of the script.

The program was written by Kohr and Sgt. Harold Dyrenfroth, both of whom also participate as actors. Pvt. Kohr was born in Oberndorf and heard the "Silent Night" story many times from the descendants of the writer and composer.

TO THE MEN OF THE 10th MOUNTAIN DIVISION:

A Merry Christmas to you all!

As we celebrate, let us rededicate our every effort to serving our fighting men overseas. Let us all pray that when another holiday season rolls around we can celebrate an old fashioned Christmas and final victory.

> J.R. Kilpatrick
> Brigadier General, U.S. Army,
> Commanding.
>
> Christmas 1944

"The years may have more than one season
    But I can remember but one,
The time when the rivers are freezin'
    And the mountains with whiteness are spun,
The snowflakes are falling so fast,
    And the winter has come now at last. . . .

Chorus

". . .Two boards upon cold powder snow, YO HO!
    What else does a man need to know?
    Two boards upon cold powder snow, YO HO!
    That's all that a man needs to know."

From a Christmas carol composed by members the 10th Mountain Division, Camp Hale, Colorado.

Christmas in Vietnam

by Patricia L. Walsh

It was not my first Christmas away from home, but it was my first in a war.

I wanted to telephone my mother and listen to her describe the fruitcakes she had baked to send to all parts of the country. I wanted to hear my brothers and sisters talk about how cold it was, and how they were ice skating on lakes and ponds so familiar to me. If I could just smell the house for a few moments, I dreamed as I helped carry a field stretcher to recovery room, just one good whiff of the Blue Spruce standing tall and beautiful in the living room.

It got bigger every year, way up to the ceiling and with branches so vast we sometimes had to trim it to get it through the kitchen door. "Now don't go cutting a big one," our mother admonished each time we headed for the grove out past the barn, hatchet in hand. "I don't want something filling up the whole house."

It was like a challenge. We waded through knee-deep snow sizing up trees and checking their shape, trying to envision them inside a room with a sofa and rocking chair already pushed aside to make space. It must be tapered just right and have cones, not prickly ones like those on the pine trees guarding our front lawn, but smooth little cones with sap so sweet you didn't mind it getting on your hands.

When we finally found it, perfectly shaped and smelling of the woods all around it, we carefully chopped it off at the base and carried it home, leaving a trail of footprints and needles in the soft snow. It was a tradition as sacred as the holiday itself, a coming together of family members who drove for hours to participate in the annual ritual.

I could see my siblings bearing it on high to the house, comparing it to trees of Christmases past. And I heard their laughter when mother opened the kitchen door and saw it.

"You're not bringing that into my house!" she would say, the same as she always did. "I'm having nothing to do with it!"

"C'mon Mom, it just looks big out here," one of my brothers would answer. "Wait till we get it set up."

They would coax it through the door while Mom pretended to wash dishes at the sink, rattling each cup and saucer to register her disapproval. She would stay out of the living room while our father helped shift more furniture and cut it off at the top or bottom so it could be set upright. And when it was hung with lights and tinsel and ornaments handed down through generations, all would proclaim it the best tree ever, even Mom.

We left the stretcher on the dirty floor of recovery room because there was no other space available. Danang's primitive, civilian hospital had been receiving several dozen new casualties a day, most of them women and children suffering from napalm burns, or mass trauma from buses going over land mines.

We were down to emergency rations; patients needing secondary procedures must wait in the crowded wards until we were resupplied, whenever that would be. Our small team of American, British and Swiss medical volunteers prayed that the Christmas truce both sides had promised would begin soon.

I went to the staff lounge to pick up my mail, our only relief from more casualties and less supplies. Almost daily someone received a package containing Christmas cookies, candy or homemade popcorn balls, all of which disappeared only seconds after being opened.

"I'll bet it's fruitcakes," I said as I inspected a good sized packaged addressed to me. "My mother bakes the best fruitcakes in the world."

"I hate fruitcake," one of my colleagues complained. But she watched with the other nurses and doctors crowded into the small room as I pried loose the nails holding the lightweight crate closed. When the top was off I tore at the brown wrapping paper inside.

"Good grief, how many cakes does she have in there?" another of my fellow nurses asked.

I was not speaking. There was a heavenly aroma coming from somewhere deep within the packing.

"It can't be," I said more to myself than those watching with anticipation. "I must be hallucinating."

But when I ripped open the last layer of paper there it was, a beautifully shaped, miniature Blue Spruce complete with cones.

I will never forget that moment. A dingy staff lounge in a filthy, overcrowded hospital in the middle of a war suddenly filled with the essence of home.

I read with wavering voice the letter from my sister Kitty, who had spent an entire afternoon treading through nearly waist-high snow to find the perfect tree. We tried not to notice one another's tears.

"What does the tag say?" one of my colleagues asked to break the awkward silence when the letter was finished. She pointed to a postal tag attached with a thin piece of wire.

I pulled it off, accidentally scraping myself on the tree's slender trunk as I did so. Hands that had been soiled by the dank smell of blood for almost a year now held a perfume so sweet I held them to my face and breathed it in.

"Read the tag," one of the surgeons said. "I have to get back to the O.R."

"The cardboard box this tree arrived in was pretty banged up when it got here," I read aloud as more staff members gathered to admire and smell the little tree that had journeyed halfway around the world. "We figured it would be important to someone so far away from home on Christmas so we built this crate for it. Merry Christmas, the San Francisco Fleet Post Office."

Patricia L. Walsh, a Boulder, Colorado novelist, was stationed in Da Nang, Vietnam, from 1967-68, where she was an anesthetist for the US Government, caring for wounded Vietnamese civilians. Her second book, Cemetery Picnic *will be published in late 1990. This story is from her novel,* Forever Sad The Hearts.

Joyous Memories
by Merle M. McClintock

Does any moment ever come to our later years that is quite like that one when we heard our name called by Santa and ran to him to get our present? Mine was a doll bed that Christmas . . . a glorious surprise . . . with all the bedding ready for use.

I hadn't known what was inside all the packages hidden in the house, but I did know their sizes and shapes. Nowhere had I seen any parcel that could have contained this treasure. There would be a doll for it on our Christmas tree at home tomorrow morning (never mind how I knew what was in one of the boxes under the sofa in the parlor).

As I walked home from the church with my family I looked at the stars and thought about the story of the nativity, about how my teachers had always told me in Sunday school that we ought to be especially interested in Christ's life, because the Holy Land looked so much like the country where we lived.

It was a good thing to live where shepherds tended their sheep in fields like those near the little town of Bethlehem, where stars blazed in skies as blue as those in Syria, and where I could lift up my eyes to quiet hills so like the mountains that lie round about Jerusalem.

I fell asleep that night feeling that my Christmas eve cup of joy was full.

The Red Coat and Fur Muff
by Clara Villarosa

Christmas morning finally came. It seemed forever since the two boxes had arrived only days before from Ohio. They were the biggest boxes I had ever seen, and my mother said one was for my brother Buzzy and the other was for me. They were from our daddy.

Buzzy and I tore off the brown paper, but the boxes were still wrapped in Christmas paper. The card on mine said, "Merry Christmas to My Little Girl from Daddy." Buzzy opened his box first. It was a light blue coat, double-breasted, with matching cap. While he was trying it on I opened my box. There in the tissue was the most beautiful coat I had ever seen. Red with a brown fur collar. As I took it from the box I saw a matching brown fur muff. I put on the coat and buttoned all the buttons. It fit perfectly. Then I slipped my hands into the muff. It felt wonderful, so soft and warm. It was lined in satin like the coat, and when I looked in the mirror I was beautiful. I looked like Shirley Temple or some kind of princess instead of a Little Rock girl who did not think herself very pretty. My hair had been curled for Christmas, and in that moment I was someone so special. I saw my brother in the mirror.

He looked great in his coat and cap and he was smiling, too. But he was not nearly as happy as I.

I was hot and my hands began to sweat inside the muff but I didn't mind. Finally I took off the coat, folded it, and carefully laid it atop its box under the Christmas tree. That day whenever some-one came by I modeled my coat. I hardly thought about my other toys or gifts—the coat and muff were Christmas enough for me.

Later we were to go to Aunt Lottie's for dinner, and I had to beg mother to let me wear the coat. She said that since it did not have any leggings my legs would get cold. All I had were short socks. I told her that my legs would not get cold. She said the coat didn't have a hat. I said I didn't need a hat. I realized then that mother was not happy about my daddy's gifts. I later overheard her talking to Cousin Anna. "Why, the nerve of him sending those children Sun-day coats for Christmas." They stopped talking when I passed the door.

Brother Harry, Aunt Lottie's husband, came to pick us up for dinner. I was so happy he was coming, because he was the only one in the family with a car. I sat in the front seat near the heater so my legs and head would keep warm. I kept my hands inside the muff the whole way to their house.

When we got there it smelled so good . . . turkey, hot rolls and pound cake all at the same time. My aunts, uncles and cousins said I looked beautiful in my coat, and I wanted to keep it on all after-noon. I was starting to feel a little sad about it, though, because mama seemed so unhappy. My cousins asked to play with the muff, but I only let them put their hands inside for a little while. I put the coat on the bed with the other coats but every once in awhile I went to the bedroom just to rub the fur on the collar and muff.

My aunts and mother were talking in the kitchen about my father. They said he hadn't cared about his family or he would not have gone off and left us like he did and not tell us where he was. The money that finally started to come was not enough. He never called . . . and now these coats! Children have to eat, have a roof over their heads and have clothes. Besides, they said, can sister (that is what they called me) wear that coat to school? Why, a Sunday coat with no leggings and no hat made little sense. He should have sent gloves instead of a muff. I guess mother and my aunts were still mad at daddy. I stopped listening when I heard mother say that the coat *just* fit, so next year I wouldn't even be able to wear it. After dinner when brother Harry drove us home my legs were cold, but I didn't say anything.

That night I lay awake thinking about our life before daddy left. We had a nice big apartment. We seemed happy then, although daddy had lost his job as a bellhop at a big hotel downtown. It was after the depression, and he could only find odd jobs.

Because cousin Anna brought leftovers from the family she worked for, and on Saturdays brother Harry gave us lots of vegetables he had culled from his grocery store, we always seemed to have enough food.

Then one day daddy went out to look for work as usual, and he never came back. We waited and waited but he never came back. Mama called the police and then the hospitals, but no one had found him. Two months later we had to move out of the apartment because there was no one working who could sign the lease.

We moved into four rooms in a run-down neighborhood and I had to change schools. Buzzy and I slept in the dining room, mother slept in the living room, and my cousin Anna in the bedroom. We were on welfare. Later, daddy told me that he left so we could be eligible for it and at least have money for rent and food. Mama was so angry and said she couldn't understand. But when we finally heard from him she seemed happy again. I guess she thought he was coming home. He sent a little money, but there was no return address on the envelope. I wished daddy would come back. I hated being on welfare. I thought everybody knew about us because we had poor clothes and I had to use stamps when I went to the store for mama.

These thoughts finally left me as I took the muff off the shelf, put it beside me in bed, and fell asleep.

After Christmas mama bought me a hat, but it didn't match the coat. Sometimes when I spent the weekend with Aunt Lottie she left me wear the coat. Brother Harry always took me out in the car, and I sat in the front seat with my hair curled, feeling so special. He called me "princess" and told everybody how pretty I was.

I outgrew the coat after wearing it to Sunday school only a few times. The weather had to be just right, mama said, and someone had to pick us up in a car.

Daddy came back a little less than a year after he'd left. He seemed so sorry for leaving and worked real hard to make it up to all of us. I wonder if mama ever forgave him, although they really worked together to make us happy and comfortable. Mama always worked after that, and once I heard her say, "you can't depend on men." She was always insisting that I get an education so I could be independent.

I was never able to tell daddy my feelings about the coat and muff. We had some long talks after I became an adult, and he was finally able to say how much he loved me and how proud he was of my accomplishments. He said he had a hard time showing affection because his parents hadn't shown much to him. I am certain that the coat was his way of saying, "I love you, Clara, you are a special little girl who deserves pretty things."

Clara Villarosa is an entrepreneur and President of the Hue-Man Experience, an African-American specialty bookstore in Denver. She is a practicing psychotherapist and the mother of two adult daughters.

The Memory Power of Christmas

by Pete Smythe

Christmas memories have strength, staying power. When I am asked to "think back" and I ask my memory center to cooperate, I am always pleasantly rewarded. Vivid videos appear to my inner eye. What a miracle!

Allow me to try a few. Begin with the year 1918. I see the Episcopal church in Glenrock, Wyoming. The Christmas tree is bedecked with wax candles, strings of popcorn, cranberries, and cutouts of angels. Three boys in costume are singing "We Three Kings" in a high, frightened tremolo. One of them is me. The one with the staff.

Very good. Now take me back to 1922. The scene is Smythe's General Store, Main Street, Glenrock, Wyoming, owned and operated by my parents Maud and Davie. Everyone works to make the Christmas season something special. My tasks are to help decorate the store and display windows, open boxes in the storeroom, and re-stock shelves. One day I open a box to find a model train set. I quickly renail the lid. The train, with my name on it, is under the tree Christmas morning.

In the good old days customers phoned in their orders. I can see myself, the delivery boy, driving from house to house in that wonderful Model-T Pickup truck.

All right, memory, give me another example of your remarkable capacity. Presto! It is my first year away at college at The University of Colorado, Boulder. The year, 1930. My transportation, the same Model-T pickup that delivered goods and groceries for the folks' general store.

It is about 300 miles from Boulder to Glenrock, but the trip seems short. I am going home for the holidays! Back to the family!

Hugs and kisses. "Welcome. You look great. How's college? Did you get homesick?"

The main meeting place at our house was the kitchen. The cook stove was fueled by wood and coal. When growing up it was one of my chores to keep the woodbox and coal scuttle filled. But now the hero has come home for a visit. The rewards are ample. We talk and we laugh and drink homemade lemonade and eat Mother's fantastic fried chicken, apple pie and fudge. On Christmas Day my dad serves the "liquid" for a special toast to our "good health and good will." The liquid is drawn from a keg of Dandelion wine in the cellar, brewed from an ancient Irish recipe.

1935. How's your recall? The swiftly moving years multiply the joys of Christmas. Marriage, and Peggy Simpson becomes Peggy Smythe. Now there are two families to join in celebration. Pete Junior and Brooke are born.

1946 finds us owning a guest ranch near Bailey, Colorado. The North Fork of the South Platte flows within a hundred feet of the front door of the lodge . . . the sights and sounds are lovely. We cut the family tree from our own little forest.

1948, La Quinta Hotel, near Palm Springs, California. We rent a small cottage in a beautiful date grove. My job at the hotel is wrangling horses and dudes in the daytime and playing piano in the bar at night. We are short of cash but long on spirit. Christmas Eve we gather around a bonfire with neighboring families and smash Pinatas.

Many Christmases have since come and gone, each holding a special magic. Years ago I wrote a song to express my thoughts about the quiet power of the Christmas season:

> Children coasting on the glist'ning snow
> Smiling faces with a warm hello
> Sweethearts kissing 'neath the mistletoe
> That's Christmas to me
>
> Flick'ring shadows of an open fire
> Old bell ringing in the White Church Spire
> Joyous carols by the Village choir
> That's Christmas to me
>
> The tiptoe of the children in the morning
> As they hurry down to see the Christmas tree
> Their whispers and their laughter are like
>   music to me
> As they open every present merrily

Johnny Snowman with his hat and cane
Frosty patterns on the window pane
Daddy playing with the 'letric train
That's Christmas to me.

Pete Smythe has been a Colorado radio, TV, and public figure for over fifty years. He has published several books, made an album, and is known to viewers statewide as the "Voice of First Federal Savings Bank." His total commitment to community service reflects his generous spirit.

CHRISTMAS FOR
COWBOYS

At Home on the Range

Christmas Fudge
by Ralph Moody

Mother used to let Grace and me take the money to pay the grocery bill every Saturday. Mr. Blaisdell always gave us a little bag of candy when we came in. I liked all kinds of chocolate, but I liked the bitter kind Mother baked cakes with best. The last Christmas before we came west, she had made fudge with some of it. It was the best candy I ever tasted. I got thinking about fudge, and one night I asked her when she was going to make some more. She said maybe she'd make some when Christmas came, but sugar cost too much to be using it up in candy we didn't need.

The more I thought about fudge, the more I thought about the bar of Baker's chocolate we got with our last groceries, and the more I wanted some of it. Baked beans, pea soup, and fried side-meat had tasted all right before, but thinking about chocolate, they didn't even make me feel hungry.

The next afternoon I was helping Father and I began day-dreaming about chcolate again. It was right then I got the idea: If I should whack a chunk off the end of that bar of chocolate, Mother would be sure to miss it. Then, before she had any idea who had done it, I could confess and probably wouldn't even get a spanking . . . I waited till she was out feeding the chickens, then told Father I was thirsty and thought I'd go in for a drink of water. All the time I was going into the house and getting the bar of chocolate down out of the cupboard, my head kept wanting to think about other things, but I wouldn't let it because I told myself that was only when you did things you shouldn't and then lied about it. I wasn't going to lie at all about the chocolate.

I heard Mother coming just when I had the knife ready to whack off the end of the bar, so I had to slip it into the front of my blouse and pick up the water dipper quick. Before I went back to help Father I went to the barn and hid the bar of chocolate in back of the currycomb box. All the rest of the afternoon, I didn't like to look at Father. Every time he spoke it made me jump, and my hands got shaking so I couldn't hold the pieces still enough for him to solder. He asked me what was the matter, and I told him it was nothing except that my hands were getting cold. I knew he didn't believe me, and every time he looked my way my heart started pounding, because he could always tell what was going on inside my head. I didn't want the chocolate anymore; I just wanted a chance to put it back without being caught.

On the way out [to get] the cows, my heart started pounding so hard, and I couldn't think. I hadn't really stolen the whole bar of chocolate, because I had only meant to take a little piece, and that's as much as I would have taken if Mother hadn't come in just when she did. If I put back the whole bar, I wouldn't have done anything wrong at all. I'd nearly decided I would do it, but just thinking so much about chocolate made my tongue almost taste the smooth bitterness of it. It didn't seem as if it would be very wrong if I only took a small piece. Then I got thinking that if I took a sharp knife and cut about half an inch off the end—with a good clean slice— Mother might never notice it. I was nearly out to where the cows were picketed when I remembered what Father had said. Some of the money in his pouch was mine because I had earned it. Why wouldn't it be all right to figure that the bar of chocolate had been bought with my own money, and in that way I wouldn't be stealing it at all. That seemed to fix everything, and I got planning how I would go out to the barn every night after school and whittle off a little piece of chocolate. . . . It was dark as tar inside the barn, but I felt along the wall for the currycomb box, and lifted the chocolate box out from behind it. . . . I shook the bar out of the box, unwrapped it, and laid it on the lower rail of the corral fence. Just as I was starting to cut it with the axe, Father said, "Son!" I couldn't think of a thing to say, but I grabbed up the bar of chocolate and shoved it inside the bib of my overalls before I turned around. He picked me up by the shoulder straps—just as he'd have picked up a kitten that had wet on the floor—and took me over to the wood pile. I didn't know anybody could spank as hard as he spanked me with that little piece of board. It felt as if my bottom were going to catch fire at every lick.

Then he stood me down and asked me if I thought I'd deserved it. He said it wasn't so much that I took the chocolate, as it was the way I took it, and because I tried to hide it when he spoke to me. But it was the next thing he said that hurt me worse than the spanking.

He said, "Son, I realize a lot better than you think I do that you have been helping to earn the living for the family. We might say the chocolate was yours in the first place. If you had asked Mother or me for it, you could have had it without a question, but I won't have you being sneaky about things. Now if you'd rather keep your own money separate from the family's, so you can buy the things you want, I think it might be a good idea."

I never knew till then how much I wanted my money to go in with Father's. Ever since we bought the cows, I had been able to feel I had a part in all the new things we were buying to make ourselves real ranchers, and it looked as though it were all slipping away from me. I had felt I was beginning to be a man, but I guess I was still just a baby, because I hid my face against Father's stomach and begged him to let me put my money in with his . . . he choked a little before he answered me. He said he didn't want a sneaky partner, but if I could be open and above board he didn't know a man he'd rather be in business with.

I couldn't help crying some more when he told me that; not because my bottom was still burning, but just because I loved him. I told him I'd never be sneaky again. We walked to the house together. At the bunkhouse door he shook hands with me, and said, "Good night, partner." When I went to sleep, my hand was still hurting—good—from where he squeezed it when we shook hands. . . .

Christmas Eve, Mother told us we couldn't get up till daylight, but when the sun first peeked over Loretta Heights we were all dressed and waiting inside the bunkhouse where we slept. Father and Mother were still in bed when we went tearing into the house. There was a big Christmas tree in the corner all decorated with strings of popcorn and whole cranberries . . . and there was a big stack of presents under it, but Father said he never even heard the sleigh bells when Santa Claus came.

We all got new shoes and caps with earlaps and stockings and heavy winter underwear. And I got a jacknife with two blades, and a new geography book . . . Mother baked a whole ham, and we had all the trimmings to go with it . . . and a big plate of fudge.

Ralph Moody wrote numerous novels set in the early 20th century American West. Born in 1898, he recounted his boyhood spent on a Colorado ranch in an autobiographical novel Little Britches, *from which this selection is taken.*

Christmas for Cowboys

by John Denver

Tall in the saddle to spend Christmas Day,
Drivin' the cattle o'er the snow-covered plains.
All of the good gifts given today,
Ours is the sky and the wide-open range.

Back in the cities they have different ways,
Football and eggnog and Christmas parades.
I'll take my blanket and I'll take the reins,
It's Christmas for cowboys on the wide open plains.

A campfire of warmth as we stop for the night,
The stars overhead the Christmas tree lights.
The wind sings a hymn as we bow down to pray,
It's Christmas for cowboys on the wide open plains.

It's tall in the saddle to spend Christmas,
Drivin' the cattle o'er the snow-covered plains.
So many gifts have been opened today,
Ours is the sky and the wide-open range.
It's Christmas for cowboys and wide open plains.

Stubby Pringle's Christmas
by Jack Schaefer

Stubby Pringle, spurs ajingle, jogs upslope through crusted snow. The roan, warmed through, moves strong and steady under him. Line cabin and line work are far forgotten things back and back and up and up the mighty mass of mountain. He is Stubby Pringle, rooting tooting hard-working hard-playing cowhand of the Triple X, heading for the Christmas dance at the schoolhouse in the valley.

He tops out on one of the lower ridges. He pulls rein to give the roan a breather. He brushes an icicle off his nose. He leans forward and reaches to brush several more off sidebars of old bit in the bridle. He straightens tall. Far ahead, over top of last and lowest ridge, on into the valley, he can see tiny specks of glowing allure that are schoolhouse windows. Light and gaiety and good liquor and fluttering skirts are there. "Wahoo!" he yells. "Gals an' women an' grandmothers!" he shouts. "Raise your skirts and start askipping! I'm acoming!"

He slaps spurs to roan. It leaps like mountain lion, out and down, full into hard gallop downslope, rushing, reckless of crusted drifts and ice-coated bush branches slapping at them.

He is Stubby Pringle, born with spurs on, nursed on tarantula juice, weaned on rawhide, at home in the saddle of a hurricane in shape of horse that can race to outer edge of eternity and back, heading now for high jinks two months overdue. He is ten feet tall and the horse is gigantic, with wings, iron-boned and dynamite-fueled, soaring in forty-foot leaps down the flank of the whitened wonder of a winter world.

They slow at the bottom. They stop. They look up the rise of the last low ridge ahead. The roan paws frozen ground and snorts twin plumes of frosty vapor. Stubby reaches around to pull down fleece-lined jacket that has worked a bit up back. He pats right-side saddlebag. He pats left-side saddlebag. He lifts reins to soar up and over last low ridge.

Hold it, Stubby. What is that? Off to the right.

He listens. He has ears that can catch snitch of mouse chewing on chunk of bacon rind beyond the log wall by his bunk. He hears. Sound of axe striking wood.

What kind of dong-bonging ding-busted dang-blatted fool would be chopping wood on a night like this and on Christmas Eve and with a dance under way at the schoolhouse in the valley? What kind of chopping is this anyway? Uneven in rhythm, feeble in stroke. Trust Stubby Pringle, who has chopped wood enough for cookstove and fireplace to fill a long freight train, to know how an axe should be handled.

There. That does it. That whopping sound can only mean that the blade has hit at an angle and bounced away without biting. Some dong-bonged ding-busted dang-blatted fool is going to be cutting off some of his own toes.

He pulls the roan around to the right. He is Stubby Pringle, born to tune of bawling bulls and blatting calves, branded at birth, cowman raised and cowman to the marrow, and no true cowman rides on without stopping to check anything strange on range. Roan chomps on bit, annoyed at interruption. It remembers who is in saddle. It sighs and obeys. They move quietly in dark of night past boles of trees jet black against dim grayness of crusted snow on ground. Light shows faintly ahead. Lantern light through a small oiled-paper window.

Yes. Of course. Just where it has been for eight months now. The Henderson place. Man and woman and small girl and waist-high boy. Homesteaders. Not even fools, homesteaders. Worse than that. Out of their minds altogether. All of them. Out here anyway. Betting the government they can stave off starving for five years in exchange for one hundred sixty acres of land. Land that just might be able to support seven jackrabbits and two coyotes and nine rattlesnakes and maybe all of four thin steers to a whole section. In a good year. Homesteaders. Always out of almost everything, money and food and tools and smiles and joy of living. Everything. Except maybe hope and stubborn endurance.

Stubby Pringle nudges the reluctant roan along. In patch light from the window by a tangled pile of dead tree branches he sees a woman. Her face is gray and pinched and tired. An old stocking cap is pulled down on her head. Ragged man's jacket bumps over long woolsey dress and clogs arms as she tries to swing an axe into a good-sized branch on the ground.

Whopping sound and axe bounces and barely misses an ankle.

"Quit that!" says Stubby, sharp. He swings the roan in close.

He looks down at her. She drops axe and backs away, frightened. She is ready to bolt into two-room bark-slab shack. She looks up. She sees that haphazard scrambled features under low hatbrim are crinkled in what could be a grin. She relaxes some, hand on door latch.

"Ma'am," says Stubby. "You trying to cripple yourself?" She just stares at him. "Man's work," he says. "Where's your man?"

"Inside," she says; then, quick, "He's sick."

"Bad?" says Stubby.

"Was," she says. "Doctor that was here this morning thinks he'll be all right now. Only he's almighty weak. All wobbly. Sleeps most of the time."

"Sleeps," says Stubby, indignant. "When there's wood to be chopped."

"He's been almighty tired," she says, quick, defensive. "Even afore he was took sick. Wore out." She is rubbing cold hands together, trying to warm them. "He tried," she says, proud. "Only a while ago. Couldn't even get his pants on. Just fell flat on the floor."

Stubby looks down at her. "An' you ain't tired?" he says.

"I ain't got time to be tired," she says. "Not with all I got to do."

Stubby Pringle looks off past dark boles of trees at last low ridgetop that hides valley and schoolhouse. "I reckon I could spare a bit of time," he says. "Likely they ain't much more'n started yet," he says. He looks again at the woman. He sees gray pinched face. He sees cold shivering under bumpy jacket. "Ma'am," he says. "Get on in there an' warm your gizzard some. I'll just chop you a bit of wood."

Roan stands with dropping reins, ground-tied, disgusted. It shakes head to send icicles tinkling from bit and bridle. Stopped in midst of epic run, wind-eating, mile-gobbling, iron-boned and dynamite-fueled, and for what? For silly chore of chopping.

Fifteen feet away Stubby Pringle chops wood. Moon is rising over last low ridgetop and its light, filtered through trees, shines on leaping blade. He is Stubby Pringle, moonstruck maverick of the Triple X, born with axe in hands, with strength of stroke in muscles, weaned on whetstone, fed on cordwood, raised to fell whole forests. He is ten feet tall and axe is enormous in moonlight and chips fly like stormflakes of snow and blade slices through branches thick as his arm, through logs thick as his thigh.

He leans axe against a stump and he spreads arms wide and he scoops up whole cords at a time and strides to door and kicks it open. . . .

Both corners of front room by fireplace are piled full now, floor to ceiling, good wood, stout wood, seasoned wood, wood enough for a whole wicked winter week. Chore done and done right, Stubby looks around him. Fire is burning bright and well-fed, working on warmth. Man lies on big old bed along opposite wall, blanket over, eyes closed, face gray-pale, snoring long and slow. Woman fusses with something at old woodstove. Stubby steps to doorway to back room. He pulls aside hanging cloth. Faint in dimness inside he sees two low bunks and in one, under an old quilt, a curly-headed small girl and in the other, under other old quilt, a boy who would be waist-high awake and standing. He sees them still and quiet, sleeping sound. "Cute little devils," he says.

He turns back and the woman is coming toward him, cup of coffee in hand, strong and hot and steaming. Coffee the kind to warm the throat and gizzard of chore-doing hard-chopping cow-hand on a cold cold night. He takes the cup and raises it to his lips. Drains it in two gulps. "Thank you, ma'am," he says. "That was right kindly of you." He sets cup on table. "I got to be getting along," he says. He starts toward outer door.

He stops, hand on door latch. Something is missing in two-room shack. Trust Stubby Pringle to know what. "Where's your tree?" he says. "Kids got to have a Christmas tree."

He sees the woman sink down on chair. He hears a sigh come from her. "I ain't had time to cut one," she says.

"I reckon not," says Stubby. "Man's job anyway," he says. "I'll get it for you. Won't take a minute. Then I got to be going."

He strides out. He scoops up axe and strides off, upslope some where small pines climb. He stretches tall and his legs lengthen and he towers huge among trees, swinging with ten-foot steps. He is Stubby Pringle, born an expert on Christmas trees, nursed on pine needles, weaned on pine cones, raised with an eye for size and shape and symmetry. There. A beauty. Perfect. Grown for this and for nothing else. Axe blade slices keen and swift. Tree topples. He strides back with tree on shoulder. He rips leather whangs from his saddle and lashes two pieces of wood to tree bottom, crosswise, so tree can stand upright again.

Stubby Pringle strides into shack, carrying tree. He sets it up, center of frontroom floor, and it stands straight, trim and straight, perky and proud and pointed. "There you are, ma'am," he says. "Get your things out an' start decorating. I got to be going." He moves toward outer door.

He stops in outer doorway. He hears the sigh behind him. "We got no things," she says. "I was figuring to buy some but sickness took the money."

Stubby Pringle looks off at last low ridgetop hiding valley and schoolhouse. "Reckon I still got a bit of time," he says. "They'll be whooping it mighty late." He turns back, closing door. He sheds hat and gloves and bandannas and jacket. He moves about checking everything in the sparse front room. He asks for things and the woman jumps to get those few of them she has. He tells her what to do and she does. He does plenty himself. With this and with that magic wonders arrive. He is Stubby Pringle, born to poverty and hard work, weaned on nothing, fed on less, raised to make do with least possible and make the most of that. Pinto beans strung on thread brighten tree in firelight and lantern light like strings of store-bought beads. Strips of one bandanna, cut with shears from sewing box, bob in bows on branch ends like gay red flowers. Snippets of fleece from jacket lining sprinkled over tree glisten like fresh fall of snow. Miracles flow from strong blunt fingers through bits of old paper bags and dabs of flour paste into link chains and twisted small streamers and two jaunty little hats and two smart little boats with sails.

"Got to finish it right," says Stubby Pringle. From strong blunt fingers comes five-pointed star, triple thickness to make it stiff, twisted bit of old wire to hold it upright. He fastens this to topmost tip of topmost bough. He wraps lone bandanna left around throat and jams battered hat on head and shrugs into now skimpy-lined jacket. "A right nice little tree," he says. "All you got to do now is get out what you got for the kids and put it under. I really got to be going." He starts toward outer door.

He stops in open doorway. He hears the sigh behind him. He knows without looking around the woman has slumped into old rocking chair. "We ain't got anything for them," she says. "Only now this tree. Which I don't mean it isn't a fine grand tree. It's more'n we'd of had 'cept for you."

Stubby Pringle stands in open doorway looking out into cold clean moonlit night. Somehow he knows without turning head two tears are sliding down thin pinched cheeks. "You go on along," she says. "They're good young uns. They know how it is. They ain't expecting a thing."

Stubby Pringle stands in open doorway looking out at last ridgetop that hides valley and schoolhouse. "All the more reason," he says soft to himself. "All the more reason something should be there when they wake." He sighs too. "I'm a dong-bonging ding-busted dang-blatted fool," he says. "But I reckon I still got a mite more time. Likely they'll be sashaying around till it's most morning."

Stubby Pringle strides on out, leaving door open. He strides back, closing door with heel behind him. In one hand he has burlap bag wrapped around paper parcel. In other hand he has squarish chunk of good pine wood. He tosses bag parcel into lap folds of woman's apron.

"Unwrap it," he says. "There's the makings for a right cute dress for the girl. Needle-and-threader like you can whip it up in no time. I'll just whittle me out a little something for the boy."

Moon is high in cold cold sky. Frosty clouds drift up there with it. Tiny flakes of snow float through upper air. Down below by a two-room shack droops a disgusted cow-pony roan, ground-tied, drooping like statue snow-crusted. It is accepting the inescapable destiny of its kind which is to wait for its rider, to conserve deep-bottomed dynamite energy, to be ready to race to the last margin of motion when waiting is done.

Inside the shack fire in fireplace cheerily gobbles wood, good wood, stout wood, seasoned wood, warming two rooms well. Man lies on bed, turned on side, curled up some, snoring slow and steady. Woman sits in rocking chair, sewing. Her head nods slow and drowsy and her eyelids sag weary but her fingers fly, stitch-stitch-stitch. A dress has shaped under her hands, small and flounced and with little puff sleeves, fine dress, fancy dress, dress for smiles and joy of living. She is sewing pink ribbon around collar and down front and into fluffy bow on back.

On a stool nearby sits Stubby Pringle, piece of good pine wood in one hand, knife in other hand, fine knife, splendid knife, all-around-accomplished knife, knife he always has with him, seven-bladed knife with four for cutting from little to big and corkscrew and can opener and screwdriver. Big cutting blade has done its work. Little cutting blade is in use now. He is Stubby Pringle, born with feel for knives in hand, weaned on emery wheel, fed on shavings, raised to whittle his way through the world. Tiny chips fly and shavings flutter. There in his hands, out of good pine wood, something is shaping. A horse. Yes. Flop-eared ewe-necked cat-hipped horse. Flop-eared head is high on ewe neck, stretched out, sniffing wind, snorting into distance. Cat hips are hunched forward, caught in crouch for forward leap. It is a horse fit to carry a waist-high boy to uttermost edge of eternity and back.

Stubby Pringle carves swift and sure. Little cutting blade makes final little cutting snitches. Yes. Tiny mottlings and markings made no mistaking. It is a strawberry roan. He closes knife and puts it in pocket. He looks up. Dress is finished in woman's lap. But woman's head has dropped down in exhaustion. She sits slumped deep in rocking chair and she too snores slow and steady.

Stubby Pringle stands up. He takes dress and puts it under tree, fine dress, fancy dress, dress waiting now for small girl to wake and wear it with smiles and joy of living. He sets wooden horse beside it, fine horse, proud horse, snorting-into-distance horse, cat hips crouched, waiting now for waist-high boy to wake and ride it around the world.

Quietly he piles wood on fire and banks ashes around to hold it for morning. Quietly he pulls on hat and wraps bandanna around and shrugs into skimpy-lined jacket. He looks at old rocking chair and tired woman slumped in it. He strides to outer door and out, leaving door open. He strides back, closing door with heel behind. He carries other burlap bag wrapped around box of candy, of fine chocolates, fancy chocolates with variegated interiors. Gently he lays this in lap of woman. Gently he takes big old shawl from wall nail and lays this over her. He stands by big old bed and looks down at snoring man. "Poor devil," he says. "Ain't fair to forget him." He takes knife from pocket, fine knife, seven-bladed knife, and lays this on blanket on bed. He picks up gloves and blows out lantern and swift as sliding moon shadow he is gone.

High up frosty clouds scuttle across face of moon. Wind whips

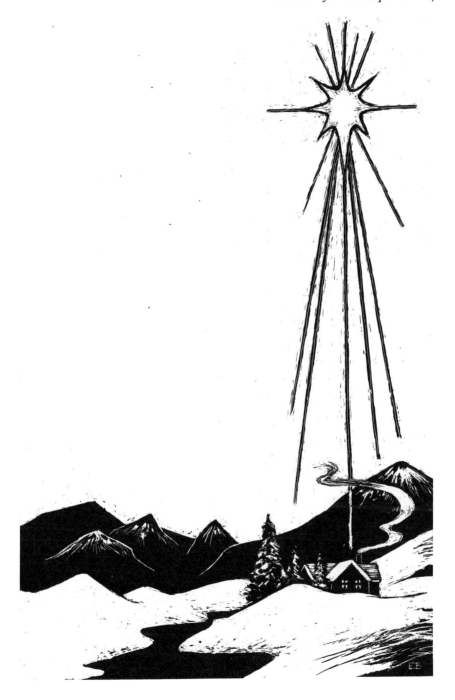

through topmost tips of tall pines. What is it that hurtles like hurricane far down there on upslope of last low ridge, scattering drifts, smashing through brush, snorting defiance at distance? It is flopeared ewe-necked cat-hipped roan, iron-boned and dynamite-fueled, ramming full gallop through the dark of night. Firm in saddle is Stubby Pringle, spurs ajingle, toes atingle, out on prowl, ready to howl, heading for the dance at the schoolhouse in the valley. He is ten feet tall, great as a grizzly, and the roan is gigantic, with wings, soaring upward in thirty-foot leaps. They top out and roan rears high, pawing stars out of sky, and drops down, cat hips lunched for fresh leap out and down.

Hold it, Stubby. Hold hard on reins. Do you see what is happening on out there in the valley?

Tiny lights that are schoolhouse windows are winking out. Tiny dark shapes moving about are horsemen riding off, are wagons pulling away.

Moon is dropping down the sky, haloed in frosty mist. Dark gray clouds dip and swoop around sweep of horizon. Cold winds weave rustling through ice-coated bushes and trees. What is that moving slow and lonesome up snow-covered mountainside? It is a flop-eared ewe-necked cat-hipped roan, just that, nothing more, small cow pony, worn and weary, taking its rider back to clammy bunk in cold line cabin. Slumped in saddle is Stubby Pringle, head down, shoulders sagged. He is just another of far-scattered poorly paid patched-clothes cowhands who inhabit these parts. Just that. And something more. He is the biggest thing there is in the whole wide roster of the human race. He is a man who has given of himself, of what little he has and is, to bring smiles and joy of living to others along his way.

He jogs along, slump-sagged in saddle, thinking of none of this. He is thinking of dances undanced, of floorboards unstomped, of willing women left unwhirled.

He jogs along, half asleep in saddle, and he is thinking now of bygone Christmas seasons and of a boy born to poverty and hard work and make-do poring in flicker of firelight over ragged old Christmas picture book. And suddenly he hears something. The tinkle of sleigh bells.

Sleigh bells?

Yes. I am telling this straight. He and roan are weaving through thick-clumped brush. Winds are sighing high overhead and on up the mountainside and lower down here they are whipping mists and snow flurries all around him. He can see nothing in mystic moving dimness. But he can hear. The tinkle of sleigh bells, faint but clear, ghostly but unmistakable. And suddenly he sees something. Movement off to the left. Swift as wind, glimmers only through brush and mist and whirling snow, but unmistakable again. Antlered heads high, frosty breath streaming, bodies rushing swift and silent, floating in flash of movement past, seeming to leap in air alone needing no touch of ground beneath. Reindeer? Yes. Reindeer strong and silent and fleet out of some far frozen northland marked on no map. Reindeer swooping down and leaping past and rising again and away, strong and effortless and fleeting. And with them, hard on their heels, almost lost in swirling snow mist of their passing, vague and formless but there, something big and bulky with runners like sleigh and flash of white beard whipping in wind and crack of long whip snapping.

Startled roan has seen something too. It stands rigid, head up, staring left and forward. Stubby Pringle, body atingle, stares too. Out of dark of night ahead, mingled with moan of wind, comes a long-drawn chuckle, deep deep chuckle, jolly and cheery and full of smiles and joy of living. And with it long-drawn words.

"We-e-e-l-l-l do-o-o-ne . . . pa-a-a-artner!"

Stubby Pringle shakes his head. He brushes an icicle from his nose. "An' I didn't have a single drink," he says. "Only coffee an' can't count that. Reckon I'm getting soft in the head." But he is cowman through and through, cowman through to the marrow. He can't ride on without stopping to check anything strange on his range. He swings down and leads off to the left. He fumbles in jacket pocket and finds a match. Strikes it. Holds it cupped and bends down. There they are. Unmistakable. Reindeer tracks.

Stubby Pringle stretches up tall. Stubby Pringle swings into saddle. Roan needs no slap of spurs to unleash strength in upward surge, up up up steep mountainside. It knows. There in saddle once more is Stubby Pringle, moonstruck maverick of the Triple X, all-around hard-proved hard-honed cowhand, ten feet tall, needing horse gigantic, with wings, iron-boned and dynamite-fueled, to take him home to little line cabin and some few winks of sleep before another day's hard work. . . .

Stubby Pringle slips into cold clammy bunk. He wriggles vigorous to warm blanket under and blanket over.

"Was it worth all that riding?" comes voice of Old Jake Hanlon from other bunk on other wall.

"Why, sure," says Stubby. "I had me a right good time."

All right, now. Say anything you want. I know, you know, any don-bonged ding-busted dang-blatted fool ought to know, that icicles breaking off branches can sound to drowsy ears something like sleigh bells. That blurry eyes half asleep can see strange things. That deer and elk make tracks like those of reindeer. That wind sighing and soughing and moaning and maundering down mountains and through piny treetops can sound like someone shaping words. But we could talk and talk and it would mean nothing to Stubby Pringle.

Stubby is wiser than we are. He knows, he will always know, who it was, plump and jolly and belly-bouncing, that spoke to him that night out on wind-whipped winter-worn mountainside.

"We-e-e-l-l-l do-o-o-ne . . . pa-a-a-art-ner!"

Author and newspaper editor Jack Schaefer is perhaps best known for the classic western novel Shane.

Christmas Eve at the Ranch
by Bill May

Christmas eve here on Elk River.
Stock is all a doin' fine.
Can hear the owl a hootin'
Atop the lonesome pine.

Snowed another foot last night.
Top fence wire just disappeared
But the sun came out again today—
A relief, 'cuz us boys feared

We'd lose track of our sled road
To that hay stack up on the hill.
(Already finished feedin' that far one
Way over by the mill.)

Just been out to turn the feed team loose.
(I'd kep' 'em in till they'd cooled down;
They was sweated up a bit
From the sled trip into town.)

The kids from Church—they sure had fun
Singin' carols on the sled.
(Thought sure that we'd meet Santa 'long the trail
'Fore I got 'em home to bed.)

But what we thought was Santa's reindeers
Was just a bunch of elk
A eatin' up the hay we'd gave
To that ol' cow we milk.

Moon's a shinin' full tonight;
The frost sparkles in its glow.
Reminds me of the light that shone
This night, so long ago.

That lit the trail to Bethlehem
That all mankind might see
The way God planned for us to go—
Lit the way for even me.

Jus' like our snowed in sled road,
I know it's there ('tho-to me-it's sometimes sorta
    dim)
If I believe in One who made that trail an' paid the
    price
That trail will lead me in.

Yes, we'll make it through the Winter
'Spite of all the snow and all our sin.
Faith in Our Trail Blazer'll get us through
To God's Eternal Spring.

From *Over the Bridge* Volume I

Descendant of Routt County pioneers, Bill May was born and raised on his family's Bar-S Ranch in the Elk River Valley. May has received national recognition as a performing folk artist, and has published several books.

All I Want For Christmas

by Baxter Black

All my clothes are laundry
All my socks are fulla holes
I've got t.p. in my hatband
And cardboard in my soles.

I've stuffed the want ad section
Underneath my long-john shirt
And my jacket's held together
By dehornin' blood and dirt.

The leather on my bridle's
Been fixed so many times
My horse looks like that fence post
Where we hang the baler twine

When I bought that horse he was
As good as most around
But when I sold 'im last month
He brought thirteen cents a pound.

I've been unable lately
To invest in purebred cows
Since my ex-wives and their lawyers
Are dependents of mine, now.

See, my first wife took my saddle
The second skinned my hide
The third one got my deer head
And the last one took my pride.

I've had a run of bad luck
But I think it's gonna peak
'Cause my dog that used to bite me
Got run over just last week.

So all I want for Christmas
Is whatever you can leave
But I'd settle for a new wife
Who would stay through New Year's Eve.

A former veterinarian and sorry team roper, Coloradan Baxter Black is one of the West's foremost Cowboy poets.

They Hung Their Stockings on the Rail
by Dave Fishell

It didn't look good.

Snow was already falling as the engineer brought the train to a stop at the station outside of Russell, Kansas, in the early morning hours of Dec. 24, 1878.

On down the tracks, towards the west and the Colorado border, lay a blue-black sky, a sure sign the weather wouldn't be improving.

When the train halted, a poorly dressed woman and two small children, bundled up against the wind, climbed aboard the lone passenger coach. After they took their places on a wood bench at the rear of the car, the children began to stare inquisitively at the three men already on board. Towards the front sat a cowboy, dressed in rough clothes, hands and face chapped and scarred by a life spent outdoors on horseback. Nearby snoozed a wealthy rancher, clad in an expensive sheepskin coat, a fancy Stetson and elegantly carved boots. Just a seat or two away from the children sat a derby-hatted drummer, the Old West's version of a traveling salesman.

When the allotted time for the stop was up, the conductor yelled "board." The engine and its three cars lurched away from the station and chugged west towards Denver and the worsening storm.

As the train gained speed, the three men in the passenger car introduced themselves to the lady and her children. And in turn the woman told a little about herself. She mentioned how she had been trying to keep a small Kansas ranch in operation several years after her husband died.

However, the work had become too much, the money too little. After trying odd jobs such as sewing in a few Kansas towns, she finally decided to move to Denver so she and the kids could live with her mother. Once in Denver she hoped to borrow $100 and start her own sewing shop.

Talk kept the passengers busy for part of the day, and at first they didn't notice the increasing wind, the thickening snow. As the train passed the Colorado line however, it was obvious the slowing train wasn't going to keep its schedule of arriving in Denver late Christmas Eve.

Late that afternoon the locomotive plowed into a deep cut and smacked headlight first into the huge snow drift piled into place by the howling wind. The engine puffed a few clouds of gray-white smoke and then came to a complete halt.

One crewman bundled up and started walking west along the tracks, hoping to reach a telegraph-station a few miles away so a snowplow could be summoned. When the conductor told the passengers they'd be spending the night on the train, tears started streaming down the faces of the two children. They had been looking forward to going to Grandma's house, unwrapping presents and having their first "real" Christmas.

As the thin daylight yielded to darkness, the three men spread out their coats in a spot close to the small coal-burning stove, trying to make a bed with a bit of warmth and comfort for the children. Just as the little ones were about to fall asleep, the salesman blurted out "we've got to give those children a Christmas." The two cat-tlemen quickly agreed.

"Children," said the rancher, "Santa Claus is coming around tonight. We want you to hang up your stockings."

"But we ain't got none," sobbed the little girl from under-neath the pile of coats. "Except those we got on and Ma says it's too cold to take 'em off."

"I've got two new pair of woolen socks," replied the rancher, "which I ain't never wore, and you are welcome to 'em."

But they're not our stockings, and he will fill them with things for you instead," cried the little girl.

"Lord love you," replied the rancher. "He won't bring me nothing. One of us will sit up, anyway, and tell him it's for you."

After the children had drifted off to sleep, the cowboy and rancher followed the salesman to the baggage compartment. The salesman opened up case after case of his new merchandise, and told the two men to take whatever they wanted for presents for the two children. Even though the salesman offered the items for free, the other two insisted on paying for the presents. Soon all four new wool socks were filled to overflowing with presents from the rancher, the cowboy, the salesman and from members of the train crew. And when the socks were full, more presents were spread out on the two seats nearest the sleeping kids.

One hardy trainman braved the blizzard, located a large sage-brush, and hauled the brush back to the train. The men and the mother spent part of the night decorating the simulated Christmas tree with bits of colored paper.

When the brother and sister awoke the next morning, their eyes opened wide, and their mouths even wider. The kids weren't the only ones who had been remembered, however. As the children scurried about with their new toys, the rancher presented the mother with a fancy photograph album. Tears filled her eyes as she turned the gold-edged pages. Then she let out a gasp.

On the back page of the album was a $100 bill.

This story is based on a chapter from the book "Recollections of a Mis-sionary in the Great West," printed in 1900 and written by Pastor Cyrus Brady, who was a passenger on the train. Dave Fishell is a Grand Junction author and historian.

Pappy and His Pipe

by Holger Albrethsen, Jr.

My Pappy used to smoke an ancient pipe
With Granger rought-cut in it, rich and ripe;
And he would light it with a kitchen match
Which right along the pipestem he would scratch

Until he'd formed a funny little groove
And worn the pipestem down, as if to prove
That nothing lasts forever, and it's true.
He'd buy another pipe, and start anew.

How many pipes he wore out I don't know —
But I recall, while trudging through the snow
Behind him on a crispy Christmas morn
When I was six, it seemed that life was born

Afresh, and peace would evermore prevail
If only I could follow that sweet trail
Of pungent Granger-smoke behind my Dad
Forever. 'Cept that I was just a lad;

And later I recall the barbershop
Where I and my old Pappy made a stop;
And there he got a haircut, not a shave,
'Cause dimes and nickels then were hard to save.

Well, Pappy put his pipe up on a shelf
And I, a kid of ten, amused myself
By reading stuff we didn't have at home,
And I was letting my imagination roam

When I glanced up and saw a local guy
Take Pappy's pipe and, careful, on the sly,
Remove the plug of Granger that was there
And substitute a hank of human hair

From off the floor; and silently I watched.
I didn't want to see a good joke botched
With half a dozen fellows sitting there
Just waiting for my dad to smoke that hair!

They knew as well as I did what he'd do.
The minute that the barber was all through
He'd go and get his pipe from off the shelf
And take a puff to satisfy himself.

He did, and while they waited for the joke
He lit it, puffed it, blew a ring of smoke
And took me by the hand and out the door,
Determined not to let them know the score.

They never did. He didn't even cough
Until we reached the wooden water trough
A half a block away, and then he said,
"Like poker; if they see your hand, you're dead!"

Well, Pappy's gone and his old pipe is, too;
But still I think of him, and when I do,
With all the years between, to my surprise,
A little of that smoke gets in my eyes.

Grand Junction, December, 1985

Holger "Al" Albrethsen, retired Chief Counsel of the Grand Junction, Colorado, office of the Department of Energy, has resumed his hobby of writing poetry—most of it reflecting life on the farms and ranches of his youth.

Santa Claus Goes West
Plagiarism Cowboy-Style
by Bill Barker

'Twas the night before Christmas, when clean 'crost the spread,
Not a critter was stirrin'; they slept like the dead;
The socks was all hanged in the bunkhouse real neat,
In the hopes they'd git filled with somethin' 'sides feet;
The kids was a-snorin' like sin in their bunks
Dreamin' of presents (sly little punks);
An' Maw in red flannels, an' me in my boots,
Hibernatin' away like a pair of owlhoots—
When behind the corral there rose such a ruckus,
I went fer my gun, lest a posse had tuck us.

Close to the winder, I hunkered down low,
Squinted outside—"Which way did they go?"
The moon on the tumbleweeds, covered with snow,
Glinted like eyes in a wise Navajo;
When what did my wonderin' gaze see (I hope),
But a midget stagecoach hauled by eight antelope,
With a li'l ol' driver, so plumb full of beans,
I savvied 'twas Santy, wearin' red jeans!
Fast as greased lightin', his team rattled by,
An' he hoo-rawed an' cussed in a muleskinner's cry:
"You, Trigger! Comanche! Now Brazos and Poco!
Git, Wyatt! On, Meathead Go, Bullet an' Loco
Over the bobwire, hit fer the sky!
You squirrelly brush-poppers, I'll see that you try."
Like dust-imps in drought time all join in a twister,
An' raise up a cloud like a tenderfoot blister,

So up to the ranch roof the antelope flew,
A-haulin' the coach an' St. Nicholas, too!
Rattler-quick I heard 'em up there,
Stampin' an' kickin' an' loaded fer bear.
As I pulled in my horns an' holstered my gun,
Down the ol' chimbley Nick come at a run.
He was duded in fur from Stetson to hips,
But his outfit was blackened from burnt buff'lo chips.
A warbag of toys 'bout busted his back,
An' he looked like a prospector totin' his pack.
His eyes, how fun-lovin'! His jawbones, how hairy!
His mug was all chilblains, his beak like a cherry;
His grin was drawed up like a fierce Cheyenne's bow,
An' his billygoat whiskers was white as the snow.
He built him a cig—held the bag in his teeth,
An' the smoke it encircled his head like a wreath.
He wore irons low—belt under his belly—
It bucked when he laughed, like a bowl full of chili.
He was grubby and round—a right friendly galoot,
An' I laughed when I seen him unloadin' his loot.
A wink of his eye and a twist of his head
Soon let me know I had nothin' to dread.
He didn't say much; went straight at his chore,
An' stuffed all them socks with presents galore,
An' stickin' his thumbs in the belt' crost his pot,
An' givin' a nod, up the chimbley he shot.
He mounted his coach, to his team roared, "Vamoose!"
They sashayed away like the James boys broke loose—
But I heard him a-shoutin'—that salty ol' coacher:
"Happy Christmas to all, an' to all, bueno nocher!"

*Denver-born Bill Barker was educated at Colorado University and Harvard,
and later joined the staff of the* Denver Post. *This poem is from* The
Wayward West.

A Merry Christmas To All.

CHRISTMAS
Dinner.

La Veta Hotel,

GUNNISON, COLO.,

WEDNESDAY, DECEMBER 25, 1889.

OH BRING US SOME FIGGY PUDDING

Celebrating the Feast

A woman homesteader writes about stopping at her neighbor's ranch to see what she was preparing for Christmas treats to give the sheepherders in nearby camps: "We found her up to her ears in cooking, and such sights and smells I could never describe: six roasted geese, three small boiled hams and three hens. Besides that she had several meat loaves, links of sausage, twelve loaves of rye bread, a tub of doughnuts, several fruitcakes, and also a quantity of little cakes with seeds, nuts and fruit in them, so pretty to look at and so good to taste. These had a thick coat of icing, some brown, some pink, some white."

From Letters of a Woman Homesteader, *Mrs. Elinore Stewart, December, 1911.*

LaVeta Hotel

Christmas Dinner, 1889

Blue Points.

Kalamazoo Celery.
Claret Wine.   Reisling Wine.

Hearts of Lettuce.

Oyster.   Consomme a la Jardiniere.

Barbecued Trout.   Parisienne Potatoes, matre d h

Boiled Ham.   Boiled Tongue.

Brazed Elk, Champignons Blance.
Rabbit a la Francisco.
Duck a la Maringue.
Queen Fritters, Sweet Wine

Roast Prime Ribs of Beef.
Young Pig Stuffed with Apple Sauce.
Provindeur of Turkey. Cranberry Sauce.
Antelope with Currant Jelly.

Chicken Salad Mayonaise.

Mashed Potatoes.   Baked Sweet Potatoes.
Petits Pois.   Hot Slaw.

Green Apple Pie.   Mince Pie.
Christmas Plum Pudding, Hard and Brandy Sauce.

La Veta Ice Cream.   Assorted Cake.

Fruits.   Raisins.   Assorted Nuts.   Muscat Grapes.

Chocolate with Whipped Cream.

Christmas Dinner
Dick Berryman's Saloon
Leadville, Colorado in 1888

Possum, Turkey, Roast Pig
Sweet Potatoes & Corn Dodgers

ROCKY MOUNTAIN PUNCH

5 bottles of Champagne
1 quart of Jamaican Rum
1 pint of Maraschino Liqueur
6 lemons, sliced
Sugar to taste

Mix all ingredients except for champagne and put on ice. Add Champagne right before serving. Float lemon and orange slices on top. Serves 20.

Punch as a drink came from the Indian word 'panch' meaning 'five.' During the 1600's, seamen drank 'punch' made from the ingredients: tea, arrack, sugar and lemon. Arrack was replaced with rum in the 1700's, and rum punch survives today as a major holiday item.

From Sam Arnold owner of the Fort Restaurant in Morrison, Colorado. He found the recipe in Jerry Thomas' Bar Tenders Guide, *published in 1862. Arnold is author of* Fryingpans West Cookbook *and can be heard Saturdays at 4 p.m. on Denver's KOA radio.*

BUCKHORN EMPANADAS

1 lb. ground beef, buffalo, or venison
4 med. white onions, finely chopped
2 bell peppers, finely chopped
4 hot green chilies, finely chopped
1 tbsp. oil
4 hard cooked eggs, chopped
15 ripe black olives, chopped
Paprika
Cayenne
Worcestershire Sauce
Tabasco Sauce
3 boxes Ready Mix Pie Crust
Salt and pepper

Cook ground meat, onions, peppers, and chilies in oil in a heavy skillet until meat is done. Do not overcook: season with salt and pepper. Cool slightly. Add eggs, olives, and other seasonings. Chill overnight. Prepare pastry according to directions. Roll dough thinly; cut into 3 inch rounds. Place 1 tbsp. filling on rounds; fold over and pinch together at edges with fork. Bake at 400 degrees for 15 minutes until brown or pastry is done. These may be frozen. Do not thaw before baking. Yield: 90 servings.

The Buckhorn Exchange has been housed in the same building at 1000 Osage, Denver, since 1893. Indian and Old West memorabilia, collected by Buckhorn founder Henry H. Zietz, are displayed among a huge array of animal trophies. The restaurant features food from the Old West. Recipe courtesy of Bill Dutton and Sid Levin.

OYSTERS MOUNTAIN STYLE

1 tablespoon chopped shallots
1/4 cup white wine
1/4 cup fish stock
1/2 cup heavy cream
2 to 3 tablespoons grated gruyere cheese
2 to 3 tablespoons grated parmesan cheese
Salt and freshly cracked black pepper to taste
12 ounces elk, boar, antelope or buffalo
    sausage, crumbled
24 small leaves spinach
12 shucked oysters with shells
Rock salt
Paprika-sprinkled lemon quarters

For the mornay sauce, place shallots and wine in a small saucepan. Bring to boil and cook, uncovered, until reduced by 1/2 in volume. Add fish stock. Cook until reduced by 1/2 in volume. Add cream. Cook until reduced by 1/3 or until mixture is faily thick and coats the back of a wooden spoon. Add gruyere and parmesan. Season with salt and pepper.

Saute sausage until done; drain. Steam spinach leaves lightly. Lay 2 spinach leaves in the bottom of each oyster shell. Put oysters on top. Sprinkle with sausage. Cover with mornay sauce. Place under broiler. Broiler until mornay sauce starts to brown. Serve oysters in their shells on a bed of rock salt. Garnish with paprika spiced lemon. Makes 12 appetizers.

This appetizer is served at Stein Eriksen's restaurant in Breckenridge, Colorado. Recipe courtesy of Steve Kleinman, Executive Chef and Food and Beverage Director at The Village at Breckenridge Resort. Steve was named "Chef of the Year" in 1990 by the Summit and Eagle County chapter of the American Culinary Federation.

HOLIDAY SHRIMP BALL
approximately 3 cups

one 12-ounce package cream cheese, softened
1 teaspoon Beau Monde
1 Tablespoon Horseradish
1 teaspoon Lawry seasoned salt
1/2 cup minced celery
1/4 cup green onions, finely choped
1 cup cooked shrimp (shelled and chopped)
    and/or crab and lobster meat
1/4 cup chopped parsley
12-ounce bottle seafood cocktail sauce
assorted crackers

Mix together cream cheese, Beau Monde, horseradish, seasoned salt, celery, and onion. Fold in shrimp. Shape into ball and put into small deep bowl. Cover and refrigerate for several hours or overnight.

Just before serving, pour bottled or homemade cocktail sauce over top of ball. Sprinkle parsley over sauce. Serve with crackers.

From Teasers and Appeasers, An Hors d'Oeuvre Cookbook *by Emily S. Grimes and Suzanne H. Richman*

Officers Department C.S.P.
John Clegborn, Warden.

"A Merry Christmas to All".—1903.

DINNER.

New York Counts, Raw.
Celery.

Cream of Fowl.   *Boston Clam Chowder.*
Lettuce.   *Young Radishes.*
Boiled Columbia River Salmon, Egg Sauce.

Young Turkey Stuffed.   *Cranberry Sauce.*
Roast Suckling Pig, with Spiced Apples.

Chicken Salad, Mayonnaise.

Escalloped Oysters.
Lamb Chops, with French Peas.
Bartlett Pear Fritters, Cogniac Sauce.

Browned Jersey Sweets.
Mashed Potatoes.   *Sugar Corn.*

English Plum Pudding, Hard and Brandy Sauce.
Mince Pie.   *Green Apple Pie.*
Chocolate Layer Cake.   *Marble Cake.*
Pound Cake.   *Cocoanut Cake.*
Raisins.   *Mixed Nuts.*   *Mixed candy.*   *Fruit.*
Cheese.
Coffee.

P.S.—Our Wine List is "Wine Saps."

J. E. Keefe, Steward.

German House
George A. Dumont, Proprietor
Christmas Menu, 1900

Dinner at 12:30.   Price. 35 cents.

Middle Park Trout   Baked Halibut

Consomme of Calcutta   Chicken a la Creole

Olives   Celery   Green Onions

Sugar Cured Boiled Ham
with Champagne Sauce

Boiled Salmon with Egg Sauce

Smothered Spring Chicken with Cream Sauce
Banana Fritters with Wine Sauce
Barbecued Belgian Hare with Pomme de Terre
Compote of Rice

Roast Turkey with Cranberry Sauce
Prime Rib Roast of Beef with Sweet Potatoes
Mashed and Browned Potatoes
Sweet Potatoes   French Peas
Sugar Corn

Boiled English Plum Pudding
with Brandy Sauce

Mince Pie   Green Apple Pie

Chocolate Cake   Cocoanut Cake

Fruit Cake   Pound Cake

Lemon Ice Cream   Assorted Fruits

Menu from restaurant in Idaho Springs, Colorado, 1900.

M. Sigi will give a grand ball at Colorado brewery hall Christmas eve, to which a general invitation is extended. Everything will be in the best style. Carriages will be in attendance free and may be ordered at the hall, or at Stockdorff's restaurant, Blake Street. No improper characters will be admitted. Tickets, including supper, $4, for sale at the door.

Daily Rocky Mountain News, *December 22, 1869*

FESTIVE VEAL CHOPS
Serves 4

4 trimmed veal chops - 10 oz. each
1 tsp. shallots, chopped
1 tsp. garlic, chopped
2 oz. unsalted butter
2 oz. raspberry vinegar
4 oz. dry red wine
1 & tasp. demi-glaze powder (Knorr Swiss)
1 Tbsp. tarragon

Heat a little olive oil in pan and sear chops on both sides. Turn down heat and cook chops for 5-7 minutes per side; cook to medium rare. Meanwhile, melt butter in a sauce pan and saute shallots and garlic. Deglaze pan with vinegar and reduce by half. Add tarragon, wine and demi-glaze powder. Reduce until thickened. Place chops on warm plate and spoon sauce on top.

Courtesy of Chef Steve Coakley, Henry's Restaurant, Hotel Strater, Durango, Colorado. Henry Strater founded the hotel in 1887, and it has been owned by the Barker family since 1926.

GREEK ROAST LEG OF LAMB
"A Family Tradition"

1 leg of lamb (approx. 6 lbs.)
1 T oregano
garlic salt, to taste
juice of 2 lemons
1/2 C. olive oil
2 T. Worchestershire sauce
salt and pepper

Season the leg of lamb with salt, pepper, garlic salt, and oregano on all surfaces. Place in roasting pan with a small amount of water (to just cover bottom of pan).

In a small bowl combine lemon juice, olive oil, and Worchestershire sauce. Mix well and pour over lamb.

Roast, uncovered, at 375 degrees until browned. Reduce heat to 300 degrees and baste often until done. A 6 pound leg of lamb should roast in 3-3 1/2 hrs.

Drizzle drippings over roast and serve.

This recipe is provided by Becky and Brad Brehmer, owners of The Blue Moon Bar & Grill in Grand Juntion, CO., and is a favorite of family and guests for the holidays.

HOLIDAY HENS
Six Servings

6 one or one and a half pound Cornish game hens
1 cup seasoned bread stuffing
1 cup red apples, finely diced with peel
1 cup white onions, finely diced
8 ozs. oysters, chopped coarsely
1 cup celery, diced finely
1/2 cup butter, melted
1 lb. bacon, par-boiled for 30 sec.
3 cups dry sherry
2 tsp. ginger
3/4 tsp. garlic powder or 3 garlic cloves, crushed
3 Tbs. flour
1/4 cup butter
12 kumquats, halved or quartered or zest from 3 oranges or lemons

1. Mix bread, apples, onions, oysters and celery with melted butter, using some of the butter to baste the cavities of hens before stuffing.
2. Season hens with salt and pepper. Stuff lightly and wrap each one with par-boiled bacon (approx. 3 strips per bird).
3. Marinate hens in mixture of sherry, ginger and garlic for 4-6 hours or overnight, turning occasionally.
4. Remove hens from marinade (reserve for later use) and place hens in roasting pan. Cover with foil and bake for 1 hour or until internal temperature reaches 185 degrees F.
   Baste occasionally with drippings. Remove foil during last 15 minutes to brown. Reserve drippings.
5. Melt 1/4 cup butter and stir in flour, browning slightly. Set aside.
6. Simmer kumquats or zest in reserved marinade, reducing liquid to approximately 2 cups. Add pan drippings and stir in flour/butter mixture gradually until thickened.
7. Pour sauce over birds before serving.

A New West version of a 16th-century English Christmas recipe, Holiday Hens is easier to prepare than it may seem. Courtesy of Gaylon Hoyer, Gulf Coast Cafe, 3301 East 1st Ave., Denver. This restaurant in Cherry Creek features wild game and seafood.

GIFT RABBITS

The morning event which attracted the largest crowd, was the distribution at Parson Uzzell's Tabernacle of the 2,500 or more Lamar jackrabbits, the result of the annual rabbit hunt. A few minutes after 9 o'clock the rabbits began to arrive from the freight depot loaded on great trucks. At once the demand for them began. There were old and young, lame, maimed and blind, ragged and neatly dressed and, in fact, persons of every description, race and nationality in the crowd that fell on the hunter's pot. Parson Uzzell superintended the distribution in person, and at the beginning announced that the strict rule would be adhered to, that no one was to have more than one rabbit, and only those whose appearance vouched for honest purpose in asking for the meat, or were known to be deserving of it, would be given any.

The Denver Republican, *Colorado Springs Bureau, December 26, 1899.*

COWBOY STEW
Perfect for a cold night—so easy!

In a heavy kettle (or dutch oven), over medium heat (campfire, charcoal, or at home), render the fat from four slices of bacon, diced. When bacon is nearly crisp, remove from pan and add 1 lb. or more of rabbit, elk, deer, antelope, or beef. Cut in 1-inch cubes and sprinkle with 1 T. flour, 1/2 t. salt, and 1/4 t. pepper. Brown well on all sides. Add 2 potatoes, cubed, and 1 large onion, diced. Stir well and allow onion to become limp but not browned. Add water or canned beef broth to barely cover. Simmer covered for 2 hours. Remove cover during last half hour and let liquid cook down.

Serves 4. Liquid may be thickened, if necessary.

From Recipes for the Rockies, *by Sara Clark.*

From "The Story of a Famous Expedition," by Thomas E. Breckenridge, 1848, with Fremont's expedition:

I will never forget that Christmas breakfast. We had no luxuries, but plenty of variety in meats.

Bill of Fare. Camp Desolation.

December 25, 1948.

Menu
Mule

Soup
Mule Tail

Fish
Baked White Mule
Boiled Gray Mule

Meats
Mule Steak, Fried Mule, Mule Chops, Broiled Mule, Stewed Mule,
Boiled Mule, Scrambled Mule, Shirred Mule, French-Fried Mule,
Minced Mule, DAMNED Mule, Mule on Toast (without the toast),
Short Ribs of Mule with Apple Sauce (without the Apple Sauce)

Relishes
Black Mule, Brown Mule, Yellow Mule, Bay Mule.
Roan Mule, Tallow Candles

Beverages
Snow, Snow-water, Water

It really made no difference how meats were cooked, it was the same old mule.

From Colorado Magazine, *Vol. 4, No. 3*

BEER FRUITCAKE

2 12-ounce cans Coors beer
2 cups raisins
1 8-ounce package pitted dates, snipped
1 cup dried apples, chopped
1 cup dried apricots, chopped
4 cups all-purpose flour
1-1/2 cups packed brown sugar
2 teaspoons pumpkin pie spice
1 teaspoon baking soda
1-1/4 cups butter
4 eggs
1 teaspoon shredded lemon peel
1 cup chopped walnuts

Pour *one can* of the Coors into saucepan; heat to boiling. Remove from heat. Add fruit; let stand 1 hour, stirring occasionally. Stir together flour, brown sugar, pumpkin pie spice and baking soda. Cut in butter till mixture resembles small peas. Combine eggs, the remaining can of Coors, and lemon peels; add to flour mixture, stirring well. Drain fruit mixture, reserving marinade. Fold fruit mixture and nuts into batter. Turn into greased and floured 10-inch tube pan. Bake in 300° oven about 2 hours or till cake tests done. Cool in pan on rack 10 minutes. Remove from pan; cool completely. Wrap in cheesecloth soaked in the reserved marinade, adding additional Coors, if necessary. Wrap tightly in foil. Store cake in cool place for up to 1 week before serving, remoistening cheesecloth with additional Coors as needed. Serves 24.

BROWN PALACE MACAROONS
Katie Stapleton

The highest star in the Brown's galaxy has to be their inimitable homemade macaroons. I have tested and re-tested Chef Dole's recipe to try to relieve you of any problems when you, too, make these in a home kitchen. I am pleased with my rendition. But I must admit that to savor the most drop-dead macaroons anywhere in the world, you'll have to dine at the Palace Arms Restaurant to taste the original Brown Palace Macaroons.

Macaroons are known for their versatility, as they are equally flavorful served at a mountain picnic or backyard barbecue or for your most formal spiffy dinner at home!

> 8 oz. almond paste*
> 4 oz. (2/3 cup) superfine sugar
> 4 egg whites

Two cookie sheets lined with ungreased brown paper.

*Available in 8-oz. cans or jars. usually on gourmet shelf of your supermarket.

Makes 25

Preheat oven to 325°.

In food processor bowl fitted with steel blade, place almond paste. Process until coarsely crumbled. Add superfine sugar. Process until very well blended. It is very important for almond paste and sugar each to have the same consistency. Remove to separate bowl.

Beat egg whites until stiff and glossy. Fold gently into almond-sugar mixture. With spoon or pastry bag, mound each macaroon on lined cookie sheet. Each macaroon should be about the size of a 50 cent piece. Bake 15 to 20 minutes, with only one cookie sheet at a time in an oven. Macaroons should be light gold in color. Remove macaroons with brown paper attached to cool. When cool, release macaroons by dampening with water the back of paper. Macaroons will peel off easily. Let them rest about 30 minutes and place in waxed paper-lined cookie tin to store. Of course, hide them at once to save them for company.

From Denver Delicious *by Katie Stapleton. These macaroons, along with other delicacies were prepared by Ms. Stapleton for Barbara Bush during the First Lady's visit to Denver in April, 1990.*

"THE THREE CRANBERRIES"

Three cranberries were living in a lodge together. One was green, one white, and one red. They were sisters. There was snow on the ground; and as the men were absent, they felt afraid, and began to say to each other, "What shall we do if the wolf comes?" "I," said the green one, "will climb up a shingoub (spruce) tree." "I," said the white one, "will hide myself in the kettle of boiled hommony;" "and I," said the red one, "will conceal myself under the snow." Presently the wolves came, and each one did as she had said. But only one of the three had judged wisely. The wolves immediately ran to the kettle and ate up the corn, and, with it, the white cranberry. The red one was trampled to pieces by their feet, and her blood spotted the snow. But she who had climbed the thick spruce-tree escaped notice, and was saved.

Legends of the American Indians, *by Henry Rowe-Schoolcraft*

CRANBERRY CRUNCH

2 cups fresh cranberries, rinsed
1/2 cup honey
1/3 cup soft margarine
1/2 cup brown sugar
1 cup rolled oats
2/3 cup whole wheat flour
1 tsp. cinnamon
1 tsp. lemon zest

In a medium saucepan, combine cranberries and honey. Bring to a boil and cook over low heat until berries pop, 10 to 15 minutes. Remove from heat and cool slightly.

In a food processor or a large bowl, combine margarine, brown sugar, oats, flour, cinnamon and zest until crumbly. Press one-half of mixture into an 8" by 8" square pan coated with cooking spray. Pour in the cranberry mixture. Sprinkle remaining oatmeal mixture over the top. Bake at 350° for 45 minutes or until top is browned and bubbly.

Serves 8

Per serving:

Calories	264
Fat (g)	9
Cholesterol (mg)	0
Fiber (g)	3
Sodium (mg)	105

From "Delightfully Healthmark . . . cooking for the health of it!"
by Susan Stevens, M.A., R.D.

"POMPIONS"

One of the oldest foods in American history, the pumpkin played an important role in feeding the settlers moving West.

America discovered pumpkins from the Indians who traded pumpkin seeds with early Spanish settlers. They combined pumpkin seeds, almonds, cumin seeds, popped corn, garlic and chili to season sauces.

Soups, stews, griddle cakes, fritters, breads, puddings and cakes were among the uses early pioneers found for the beloved "pompion." Records also show pumpkins were used in brewing when ingredients were scarce and regular beer could not be made.

Pumpkin stew was a favorite, made in a variety of ways. A mixture of corn, beans, green peppers, beef or chicken and fruit were stewed in pumpkin juice and served on the table in a cooked, hollowed-out pumpkin. Pumpkins were also cut into pieces, boiled, seasoned and served in a dish that resembled baked apples.

The abundance and versatility of pumpkins even prompted one pioneer to create the saying,

> "We have pumpkins at morning,
>   pumpkins at noon,
> "If it were not for pumpkins, we should
>   be undone."

From A Taste of the West from Coors

PUMPKIN PIE
"Our Family's Favorite"

2 Pies or 12 to 14 servings

Two 9-inch unbaked pie shells
3-1/2 cups canned pumpkin
1 cup firmly packed brown sugar
1 cup granulated sugar
1/4 teaspoon ground cloves
2-1/2 teaspoons ground cinnamon
2-1/2 teaspoons ground ginger
1 teaspoon salt
4 eggs, beaten
1 cup scalded evaporated milk
1 cup scalded whipping cream
Sweetened whipped cream

1. Preheat oven to 325°F.
2. In large mixing bowl, combine pumpkin, sugars, cloves, cinnamon, ginger, salt and beaten eggs. Stir well. Add scalded milk and cream. Mix thoroughly. Pour into pie shells, dividing evenly.
3. Bake for about 1 hour, or until knife inserted in center comes out clean. Serve with sweetened whipped cream to which a little rum has been added, if desired.
NOTE: This recipe may be divided in half for one pie.

Pumpkin pie with cheesecake topping: Divide recipe for Pumpkin Pie in half. In Step 2, in bowl, beat together 1 package (8 ounces) cream cheese, 1/2 cup sugar, 1 teaspoon vanilla extract and 2 eggs. Pour over pie filling before baking. Decorate with pecan halves. Bake as directed.

From The New High Altitude Cookbook, *by Beverly M. Anderson and Donna M. Hamilton.*

DECK THE HALLS

Christmas Celebrations Then & Now

A Georgetown Gala

Of course everybody is getting ready for Christmas night. There will be music and gaiety in Cushman's Opera House. "The Beauty and Chivalry" of Georgetown and the region round about will be gathered there. It will be a gala night for all who accept the invitation of Georgetown Fire and Hose Co. No. 1 and attend their first annual ball. Let everybody prepare to give the boys a fine send off and a big benefit. Tickets including carriages only $2.50. Orders for carriages to be left at Kinney's. Gorton's will furnish the music.

The Miner, Georgetown, Colorado
December 22, 1877

Oh, How We Danced . . .

The ladies were attired in the most beautiful of gowns—the topic of which all readers, and especially the ladies—are most interested. Thus, taking in a fresh supply of adjectives, and a new stock of adverbs. We begin . . . Mrs. J. L. Sanderson of St. Louis appeared in a garnet satin. Trimmed elaborately with velvet to match and black thread lace—jewels, moss agate with a massive chain and cross of gold. In our opinion she was the most expensively dressed lady in the room.

Mrs. E. H. Starrette wore a delicate rose colored silk—long, trimmed with plaitings of the same and point lace; white lace shawl, Coiffure Patti Chignon and curl with cornet of roses.

The stately Miss Ella monk wore a white alpaca, whose rich train flowed from her fair form like foam from a goblet of exquisite mold. Hers was the finest figure in the room.

Miss Josie Shackelton in an elegant green silk trimmed with ruchings of green and white appeared very prettily.

The firemen appeared in full uniform, barring, as an Irishman would say, their hats, which were hung around the room by way of additional ornament. Their gay red shirts might be seen flitting hither and thither. Now in the mazy dance, and again entertaining with lively conversation their bevies of lookers-on.

The decorations were hung richly in the spacious hall. Bathed in the light of a number of costly chandeliers. The sides of the room and pillars supporting the ceiling were garnished and garlanded with evergreens in the most profuse yet tasteful style of decorative art . . . arranged in stars, circles, triangles, and other fanciful and beautiful shapes. Scattered throughout this bower of evergreen were many canaries, whose merry carol made the place seem an hour's paradise. Without exaggeration, the room was infinitely the most beautiful in its decorations ever seen in this city on a like occasion.

The supper prepared at Charlie North's "American House Cafe" was abundant, excellent and reasonable in price. He is entitled to great credit for the manner in which it was managed.

The dancing was kept up until a very late hour, and it was four o'clock before the brilliant assemblage began finally to disperse. The music was probably the best ever had in Denver, and to the large band high praise must be rendered.

The Daily Rocky Mountain News, *December 28, 1870*

Which 'Posada' Will Have Room?

Our Lady of Guadalupe Church in Denver and other churches with Spanish heritage in Colorado, observe Christmas every year with a custom called "Las Posadas," "The Inns."

During the "novena"—nine days preceding Christmas, members of the congregation go from house to house at a certain hour every night, asking for a place for Mary and Joseph to spend the night. Young people are chosen to play the Holy Family and a donkey accompanies them on their journey. The group of pilgrims carries statues of Mary and Joseph as they look for shelter. During their journey, they sing many traditional carols in Spanish, such as these verses from one song:

> Entren santos peregrinos, peregrinos
> reciban este rincon
> no de esta pobre morada, pobre morada,
> sino de mi corazon.

> Enter holy pilgrims, pilgrims
> receive this corner
> not of this poor home, poor home,
> but of my heart.

> Esta noche es de alegria, alegria,
> de gusto y de regocijo
> porque hospedamos aqui
> a la madre de Dios hijo.

> This is a night of joy, joy
> one of happiness and rejoicing
> because we are giving shelter here
> to the mother of the Son of God.

> Amados peregrinos, peregrinos,
> Jesus, Maria y Jose,
> mi alma doy por ellos
> mi corazon, tambien.

> Beloved pilgrims, pilgrims,
> Jesus, Mary, and Joseph,
> I give my soul for them
> my heart, too.

Finally, after several refusals, the group is invited in each night by a hospitable "inn keeper" and refreshments are served while more music is shared.

The last evening of "Las Posadas" is on Christmas Eve, when the Pilgrims find their final shelter at the church. It is a fitting place for the group to celebrate the Christ Child's birth.

O Tannenbaum

Folks in the tiny town of Walden, Colorado, have reason for jubilation this Christmas of 1990 as the nation's Christmas tree is cut from their forests and sent to Washington, D.C. to stand in front of the Capitol building.

The official lighting ceremony will be hailed with pride and rejoicing by the 800 or so residents of this mountain village as a nation joins in.

Magic In The Desert

It is known to many as "The Christmas Tree," and still to others as "The Stinking Desert Christmas Tree."

It has been a visible message of Christmas goodwill to travelers through western Colorado for over three decades. Magically decorated each year during the days between Thanksgiving and Christmas, the tree has stood a noble sentinel along Highway 50 between Delta and Grand Junction.

Some say Elves decorate it, others admit that they themselves have placed ornaments upon its boughs . . . popcorn garlands, coffee can lids, aluminum foil, bows, bells, homemade and store-bought treasures all have adorned the wondrous tree.

Motorists from around the country have stopped to decorate it, and it gained national recognition when it was featured on Charles Kuralt's television program.

In 1989 Mother Nature reclaimed the tree, but the locals have since planted a new one in its place, a living symbol of the magic of yuletide in the desert.

Delta County Independent, *1989*

Luminarias Light Up Christmas
In Costilla County

In the 1890's, people living in the mountain towns of Costilla county like Chama, La Valley, San Pedro and San Luis were poor, but that didn't put a damper on their ability to celebrate Christmas. Their special activities had nothing to do with money—heritage was the key to their joyful manner of celebrating.

Luminaries or bonfires would start appearing two weeks before Christmas when the Masses for the Virgin Mary, called "Missas de la Virgen," would begin. To prepare for the luminarias some of the men would bring pitch from the mountains. When burned, this type of wood gives off a brilliant light. Once the pitch had been gathered, it would be chopped into sticks, about two feet in length, and arranged into a rectangular frame about 3 feet high. Additional sticks would be placed inside the frame. The townsmen built one luminaria after another, placing them about a hundred yards apart. Excitement filled the air as many gathered after dark to watch the lighting ceremony. The brilliantly burning fires were strung out across town, illuminating the countryside for miles.

Boys and girls who went to see the luminarias would dress up so they wouldn't be recognized. They wore masks made of rags and long overcoats or long dresses. Some of the boys, who were called "abuelos," had whips that resembled thin clubs with leather straps attached to them. The straps had a popper at the end and when the whips were cracked, they would sound loudly through the night. The abuelos wouldn't really hit anyone with their whips, but would sneak up on someone near the luminarias and crack the whips. The unsuspecting person would sink to his knees, cross his arms in front of his chest and pray for mercy.

On "Noche Buena," or Christmas Eve, children, accompanied by adult musicians, would go from home to home singing Christmas songs and doing little dances. The people whose homes they'd enter offered them cookies or empanadas filled with pumpkin custard.

A favorite Christmas event in many of the small villages of the San Luis Valley was the presentation of the play "Los Pastores," or "The Shepherds." The story was based on a 500-year-old European mystery play which was passed on through history and brought to

Costilla County from New Mexico in 1850. A simple play, its touching sincerity appealed to audiences of all ages.*

Another favorite Christmas play was based on the Bible story of Mary and Joseph fleeing with the Christ Child to escape the terrible decrees of King Herod. It was entitled "El Niño Perdido," or "The Lost Child."

People living in these mountains had a knack for combining religious devotion with fun. They might pray for hours during the Christmas season, then turn around and do something joyful. Christmas meant simple, self-improvised pleasures, based on customs handed down from generation to generation.

Based on reminiscences of Euleto Medina of San Luis, as told to Dale Payne of the Pueblo Star-Journal and Sunday Chieftain *in 1971.*

Christmas Eve On Mantey Heights
by Harold Hamel

The Christmas season is a special time for Christians throughout the world. With a wide variety of traditions and events we celebrate the birth of the Christ Child. In a small neighborhood in Grand Junction called Mantey Heights a custom has been observed each Christmas Eve for over 40 years.

*Editor's Note: The Sangre de Cristo Parish in San Luis presents "Los Pastores" in some form every year. In 1989 Arsenio Cordova came from New Mexico to give a special performance.

The neighborhood was developed with the dream of adobe homes being built in the Northern New Mexico tradition. Although this is not now the exclusive architectural style in Mantey Heights, the Northern New Mexico custom of lighting luminaries (farolitos . . . the Anglo Americans call them luminarias) on Christmas Eve continues. The tradition involves lighting candles in brown paper sacks, weighted with sand. They are placed along the roadways, driveways, and sometimes on the parapets of adobe homes to light the way for the Spirit of the Christ Child.

All of the neighbors in Mantey Heights participate in preparing and placing the thousands of luminarias which are lighted as dusk gathers on Christmas Eve and burn well into the early morning hours of Christmas Day. The beauty of the scene is difficult to describe. It changes each year as different phases of the moon provide a varied light. Some years softly falling snow adds a special eloquence. Occasionally a fierce blizzard or even rain will challenge the keepers of the luminarias to light and maintain the fire of the candles.

The streets of Mantey Heights are filled with slowly moving cars, their headlights dimmed, as residents of the neighborhood share the loveliness of the Christmas luminarias with Grand Junction and Mesa County.

Mr. Hamel, a stained-glass artist, has lived in Mantey Heights for 22 years with his wife Florence.

Editor's Note:
There has been much controversy over the correct word and the correct spelling of the word for these lights. To quote from Ruben Cobos, professor of modern languages at the University of New Mexico and a native of Mexico:

"A *luminaria* is any light which is placed in windows, balconies, towers, and streets as a sign of festivity and public rejoicing. The word is feminine in gender and the plural form—*luminarias*—is more commonly used."

The word *farolito*—small lantern—has its warm supporters, but a *farolito* cannot be a small bonfire as were the original *luminarias,* and as these festive lights are usually placed on the ground and never hung as lanterns, *luminarias* more generally is accepted.

Yuletide At Palmer Lake
by Ralph C. Taylor

The mountain town of Palmer Lake brings in the Christmas spirit every year by holding a yule log ceremony on the Sunday before Christmas. Basing their festivities on the English custom of hunting for a log that has been hidden in the forest, Palmer Lake residents have enjoyed this custom since 1933. On the Sunday before Christmas crowds gather at the Palmer Lake town hall. Some stay behind singing carols while groups of hunters wearing red and green caps go into the mountains in search of the Yule log which has been hidden by a team of two before the first snow.

There is much shouting and merriment when someone discovers the log. Ropes are attached to it and everyone joins in pulling it down the mountainside while the finder rides the log.

By the time the searchers return to the hall they are ready for the warmth of fellowship and the glow of the log, which is kindled in the fireplace with splinters from last year's log. As the flames dance around the Yule log, the hunters and all the guests drink Wassail and sing spirited carols together, sharing the warmth and brightness of the Christmas season.

Based on an article by Ralph C. Taylor in the
Pueblo Star-Journal Chieftain, Dec. 14, 1952.

May the fire of this log warm the cold; may the hungry be fed; may the weary find rest, and may all enjoy Heaven's peace.

Traditional Yule Log Prayer

Rejoice — The War Is Over!

by Edith Eudora Kohl

Each day as Christmas draws nearer, the crowds increase in size and momentum. . . . These people represent not only Denver's populace which has increased during the war. They have come from towns and farms of Colorado, Wyoming, Nebraska, New Mexico and other western states.

The store windows, dressed up in all their trimmings, are a colorful sight in which even the most practical and homely articles are displayed—blankets and boxes of tools and kettles and clothing adorned in cellophane and ribbons to look like Cinderella presents. The buying this year is running heavily to essentials—clothes, furniture and other family equipment not obtainable during the war.

An old woman in ragged coat and shoddy shoes holds a bottle of perfume in work-worn hands, smelling it again and again, pays with a soiled, tightly folded $5 bill, and has it wrapped up. "It's for my granddaughter in the Waves—I never had any perfume in my day," she explains to no one in particular. Perhaps this was not so much a gift to the granddaughter as myrrh to the spirit of Christmas—and to peace.

The war is over. A people will give thanks to the Prince of Peace with a prayer on their lips—or in their hearts, as expressed through gifts and their activities at home and among their families and friends. A candle in the soul.

And so—it is Christmastime, in Denver, the metropolis of the old frontier. Out over the ranges shepherds still watch their flocks and men ride in the silent night over which the star of Bethlehem still shines bright and low.

Denver Post, Dec. 23, 1945

Edith Eudora Kohl was a writer for The Denver Post *for many years.*

ACKNOWLEDGEMENTS

"Star of Empire Guides the Way" from *Denver's First Christmas*. Used with permission of Western History Dept., Denver Public Library.

"Pike's Yuletide Feast" from the *Journals of Zebulon M. Pike*, Univ. of Oklahoma Press.

"They Held Their Tin Cups High" by Mike Flanagan. Used with permission of author.

"Platte River Gold Diggings" from Western History Dept., Denver Public Library.

"Pioneer Celebrations Are Born" from *A Rocky Mountain Christmas* by John Monnett. Used with permission.

"Christmas Wolves on the Arkansas River" from the *Denver Post* December 23, 1929.

"Good Hopes for the Future" from the *Daily Rocky Mountain News*, December 28, 1870.

"An English Woman Goes West" from *A Diary* by Rose Kingsley. Western History Dept., Denver Public Library.

"Does Tradition Bind at Christmas?" from *Second Banana* by Dottie Lamm used with permission of author.

"Lullabye for Christmas Eve" by Lois Beebe Hayna. Used with permission of author.

A Lady's Life in the Rocky Mountains by Isabella L. Bird. University of Oklahoma Press. New Edition 1960.

"Continental Divide—December" by Enos Mills from *Adventures of A Nature Guide*, Doubleday and Co., Inc. Used with permission.

"Colorado Christmas" sung by Nitty Gritty Dirt Band. Words and music by Steve Goodman. Used with permission, Bug Music, Inc.

"Christmas Eve at the Ranch" from *Over the Bridge* Volume I by Bill May. Used with permission.

"All I want for Christmas" from *Coyote Cowboy Poetry* by Baxter Black. Used with permission.

"They Hung Their Stockings on the Rail" by Dave Fishell. *The Daily Sentinel*, Grand Junction, December 23, 1988.

"Santa Claus Goes West" from the *Wayward West* by William J. Barter. Doubleday and Co., Inc. Used with permission.

"Holiday Shrimp Ball" from *Teasers and Appeasers, An Hors d'oeuvre Cookbook*. Used with permission of authors.

"Cowboy Stew" from *Recipes for the Rockies* by Sara Clark. Used with permission.

"Mule Menu" by Thomas E. Breckenridge. Reprinted *Colorado Magazine*, Vol. 4, No. 3, Winter 1968.

"Beer Fruitcake" from *A Taste of the West from Coors*. Better Homes and Gardens. Used with permission.

"Brown Palace Macaroons" from *Denver Delicious* by Katie Stapleton. Used with permission.

"Cranberry Crunch" from *Delightfully Healthmark* by Susan Stevens, M.A., R.D. Health Mark Centers, Inc. 1989. Used with permission.

"Pumpkin Pie and Pompions" description from *A Taste of the West from Coors*. Recipe from the *New High Altitude Cookbook* by Beverly M. Anderson and Donna M. Hamilton, Random House, Inc. Used with permission.

"LaVeta," "Officers Dept.," "German House," menu used with permission of Western History Dept., Denver Public Library.

"Which 'Posada' Will Have Room?" Information and words of song provided by Bob Green, Our Lady of Guadalupe Church, Denver, and Emma Vallejo. English translation Father Lorenzo Ruiz, Vicar to Hispanics, Denver.

"Luminarias Light Up Christmas" by Euleto Medina of San Luis and Dale Payne of the *Pueblo Star-Journal and Sunday Chiefton* in 1971.

"Christmas Eve on Mantey Heights" with permission of author.

"Magic in the Desert" *Delta County Independent* and the Delta County Chamber of Commerce.

"Yuletide at Palmer Lake" from the *Pueblo Star-Journal*, December 14, 1952.

"Mt. of the Holy Cross" sketch taken from a Leadville handmade book. Used with permission of the Colorado Historical Society.

Section divider Christmas greeting cards, chapters 1, 3, 4, 5, 6, 7. Used with permission of Western History Dept., Denver Public Library.